CARRIERS

The Men and the Machines

CARRIERS
The Men and the Machines

David Miller

Lindsay Peacock

Published by Salamander Books Limited
LONDON • NEW YORK

A Salamander Book

Published by Salamander Books Ltd.,
129-137 York Way,
London N7 9LG,
United Kingdom

ISBN 0-86101-561-4

Distributed in the United Kingdom by:
Hodder and Stoughton Services,
PO Box 6, Mill Road,
Dunton Green,
Sevenoaks,
Kent TN13 2XX

All correspondence concerning the contents of this volume should be addressed to Salamander Books Ltd.

Editors: Bob Munro and Graham Smith

Designers: Phil Gorton, Paul Johnson, John Heritage, Tim Scott and Tony Jones.

Filmset by The Old Mill, London

Colour artworks: Tony Gibbons; ©Salamander Books Ltd.

Colour diagrams: ©Salamander Books Ltd.

Line-views: ©Salamander Books Ltd.

Colour reproduction by P&W Graphics Pte. Ltd., Singapore

Printed in Singapore

Acknowledgements
The publishers would like to thank Roger Chesneau for his contribution as Consultant Editor. Roger is a freelance military book editor and designer who has also written a number of books on maritime and aviation topics.

Contents

Introduction

When the Wright brothers made their historic flight at Kitty Hawk on 17 December 1903, none realized that just seven years later Lieutenant Ely, USN, would make the first take-off from a warship. By the outbreak of World War I, most leading navies were operating seaplanes from coastal bases and some, like the Royal Navy were experimenting with seaplane-carrying ships to enable aircraft to accompany the fleet to distant waters. By the end of the war carriers which could launch and recover wheeled aircraft were an accepted fact and the pattern for the development of naval air power had been established.

The technology and operating concepts of air power at sea developed through the twenties and thirties, although in a piecemeal fashion. It was only the advent of World War II that finally brought the carrier into the mainstream of naval power. Large scale strikes were launched at land installations, and huge naval battles took place where hundreds of aircraft fought above opposing ships many miles apart. The carrier had finally come of age in naval warfare.

Today the US Navy's super-carriers are the most powerful military machines in the world, with an unparalleled ability to unleash a large variety of weapons against land or sea targets.

This powerful force operates from a base that is virtually self-contained and which moves about the world's oceans with relative freedom. Land-based aircraft can, of course, be deployed to trouble spots, but they require friendly airbases within range, while a huge support organisation must also be flown out or sent by ship. The carrier, however, is independent of these and can operate at great distances from any other form of support.

However, the cost of operating a vessel such as this is huge. The ship itself is large, sophisticated and costly, but this is only the starting point. Carrier operations are manpower intensive, requiring not only the ship's crew and the flight crews, but also a large number of men to operate the flight deck and for aircraft maintenance. The total crew aboard a Roosevelt class carrier, for example, is 6,286, and the cost of paying, training and equipping such numbers is very high. Also, no carrier

can operate alone and must have a properly balanced group of escort and support ships. A typical escort group comprises between four and six air defence and anti-submarine destroyers and frigates plus a fleet replenishment ship. Finally, one carrier in a navy is insufficient, as all ships must spend considerable periods in dockyard hands for refitting or modernisation. To avoid protracted periods without a carrier at sea, an absolute minimum of two or preferably three vessels are required. The dilemma for naval staffs is thus clear: carriers are extremely effective warships, but they take up a large part of a navy's resources.

There are four main types of carrier in service today. Largest of these are the super-carriers displacing over 70,000 tons; the US Navy currently has fourteen, the Soviet Navy one. Next come the medium carriers, also operating conventional take-off and landing (CTOL) aircraft. The French currently have two, soon to be replaced by two nuclear-powered carriers, and two similar, but conventionally-powered carriers are building for the Indian Navy. There is also a decreasing number of small, elderly CTOL carriers in service with the Indian, Argentine and Brazilian Navies.

The third group is the V/STOL (vertical and short take-off and landing) carrier, operating a mix of helicopters and fixed-wing aircraft such as the Harrier/Sea Harrier an the Yakovlev Yak-38 Forger. The effectiveness of such a light carrier concept was proven in the 1982 Falklands War. Currently in this group are the British Invincible class, Soviet Kiev class, the Italian *Garibaldi* and the Spanish *Principe de Asturias*, and this number is likely to increase.

The fourth group comprises air-capable amphibious assault ships, with full-length axial flight decks, operating V/STOL fixed-wing aircraft and helicopters. Largest by far in this group is the US Navy's Wasp class, displacing 40,532tons; but a most interesting and cost-effective smaller design has recently appeared in the Italian Navy — the San Marco class.

Most of the world's major navies are continuing to develop the tactics and technology of carrier operations. The US Navy is firmly wedded to the concept of the fleet carrier group as a power projection tool, accepting the financial and manpower costs this requires. The Soviet Union is allocating major resources to create a similar capability on a smaller scale and the French are developing a new generation of nuclear-powered carrier. For most other navies, future developments will be in the use of small helicopter or V/STOL carriers, useful for ASW, air assault, air defence or light strike roles. In one form or another, the aircraft-carrying ship will be a key element of surface naval power for the foreseeable future.

1

New Frontiers

THE higher the point of observation, the further one can see. Given clear weather, this is especially pertinent at sea, where the view is not hampered by topography. It is a basic tenet of seamanship. Whether searching for a landfall, watching for natural hazards or trying to spot an enemy before he sees you, the man in the crow's nest has arguably the most important job aboard any ocean-going vessel. On board a warship, as gunnery ranges began to increase during the second half of the 18th Century, the task of artillery spotting also fell to the man aloft. Based on his reports, corrections could then be made to the aim and the chances of projectiles hitting the target accurately greatly increased.

At this time the fleet action, involving perhaps dozens of ships on either side, was seen as the decisive encounter at sea: governments could fall as a result of such a battle. Therefore, given the vastness of the waters and the relatively insignificant size of the combatant vessels, effective reconnaissance was vital. Moreover, the commander who received the first accurate accounts of the enemy's strength, disposition, speed and bearing held a distinct tactical and operational advantage; and the higher the position of the lookout the better the chance of seizing this vital advantage.

The most significant advance in maritime reconnaissance during the 1800s went barely noticed. On 3 August 1861, during the American Civil War, one John la Mountain boarded a hydrogen balloon carried by a tiny Union steamship rejoicing in the name of *Fanny* and rose several dozen feet into the air in order to observe the disposition of opposing Confederate forces at Hampton Roads, Virginia. The following year, John B. Starkweather carried out a similar operation from the small paddle steamer *Mayflower*, while the Confederate tug *Teaser* flew a manned balloon on the James River in July 1862.

Desultory experiments by most of the world's leading navies proceeded in fits and starts throughout the latter half of the 19th Century, but there was no further operational use of manned balloons until the First World War, when fear of submarines and the hazard of mines brought about the large-scale equipment of ships with manned observation balloons, let aloft or towed aft as a safety precaution. Great Britain's Royal Navy, in particular,

commissioned a large number of merchant ships, fitting them with hydrogen generation plant, winches and storage facilities, for service generally in the spotting role. Spherical balloons, which were directionally unpredictable in the air, were replaced by more stable designs which featured fins to provide a steadier platform.

It was inevitable, once the practicability of the heavier-than-air craft had been accepted just after the turn of the century, that efforts would be made to take such a machine to sea. The dramatic improvements offered by the aircraft over the balloon could hardly be disputed: independence in operation both of the wind and of the parent ship; an impressive radius of action; a multi-sortie capability (at least in theory); and, not least, the removal of the need to store highly inflammable gas reserves on board ship.

Much pioneering work was done in the years immediately preceding the First World War. In the United States, Eugene Ely demonstrated the possibilities, first by flying a Curtiss Pusher in November 1910 from a bow platform installed aboard the cruiser USS *Birmingham*, and two months later by landing a similar aircraft on a stern platform fitted to the cruiser USS *Pennsylvania*. Lt. Charles Samson, Royal Navy, emulated Ely's first achievement in January 1912 by taking off in a Short Pusher from a track rigged over the forecastle of the battleship HMS *Africa*, and in May of the same year became the

Left: The first use of ships as aircraft carriers occurred during the American Civil War. Several carriers were constructed, including this Union barge, here launching a reconnaissance balloon in November 1861.

Right Top: Flying a "Curtiss Pusher" biplane, Lieutenant Eugene B. Ely, USN, makes the historic first take-off from USS *Birmingham* in 1910.

Right Below: Lieutenant Ely was also the first to land on a ship, completing his historic double on 18 January 1911, when he landed his Curtiss Pusher on USS *Pennsylvania*.

first man to perform the feat from a ship under way when he flew from the battleship HMS *Hibernia*. On neither occasion were landings attempted.

It is important to stress that these flights were conducted by wheeled aircraft, albeit fitted with flotation gear for Samson's ventures. They were also, perforce, carried out aboard large ships, since only these would accommodate flying-off and landing-on platforms and tracks deemed to be of adequate length. However, all this aeronautical gear was extemporary: it compromised the fighting capabilities of the ships, in particular the main armament, and was thus dismissed by most commanders as being of little practical value.

More encouragement was given to the development of the seaplane (hydroaeroplane in the parlance of the day) for fleet use, and by the outbreak of the First World War, France, the United Kingdom and Japan had all gained useful experience in the operation of seaplanes from ships. The French *Foudre*, a former torpedo-boat transport and sometime repair ship, minelayer and balloon ship, had an aircraft hangar fitted in early 1912 and later a forecastle platform. The British *Hermes*, an obsolete protected cruiser, was fitted out as a seaplane carrier by May 1913, a launching ramp for trolley-assisted take-offs being installed over the forecastle and canvas screening to protect her frail aircraft being added forward and aft, together with handling derricks. The Japanese *Wakamiya* was a British freighter seized as a prize during the Russo-Japanese War of 1904 – 05 and equipped with derricks and stowage facilities for seaplanes during 1913. These three vessels were all employed by their respective navies in trials and manoeuvres during 1913, offering valuable information as to the practicalities of operating military aircraft at sea.

Thus, in embryonic form, the essential characteristics of the modern aircraft carrier were in being, and under evaluation, prior to the First World War: the flying-off and landing-on platforms; the hangar,

Below: A Sopwith 1½-Strutter of the Royal Naval Air Service is launched from an early British aircraft carrier during World War I. The skid undercarriage ran in a trolley down the rails seen on the flight deck.

The first *Ark Royal*.

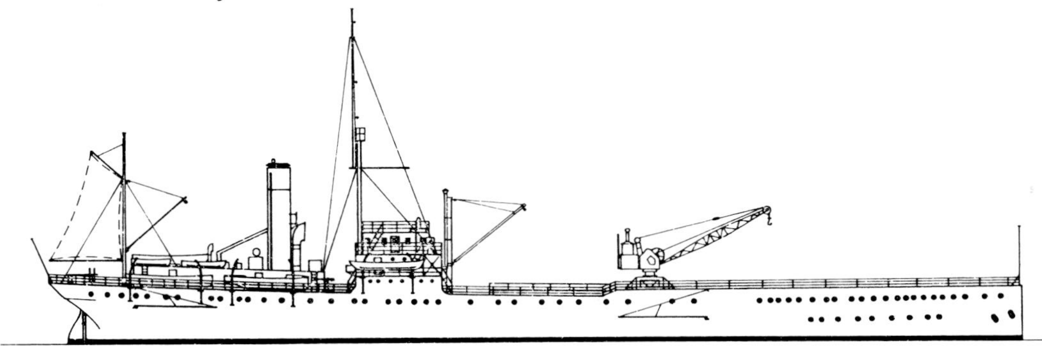

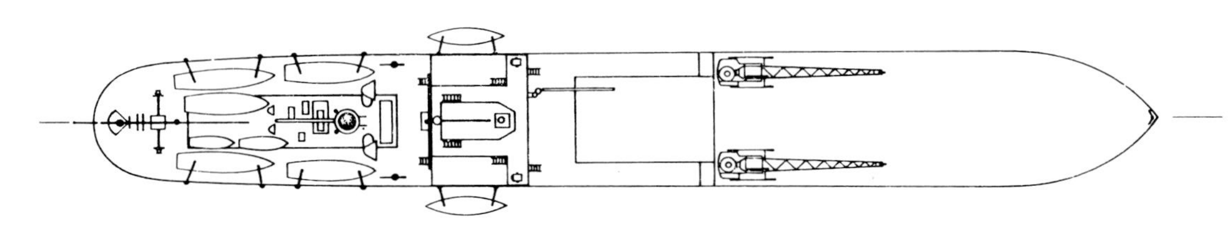

Left: HMS *Ark Royal* (7,450tons), the Royal Navy's first warship built specifically to operate aircraft. She was under construction as a collier when she was bought by the Admiralty and totally redesigned; the machinery and superstructure were moved aft, leaving a large aircraft hold forward. Aircraft were lifted from the hold by a crane and were then either launched from the flight-deck or, in the case of seaplanes, lifted over the side.

***Ark Royal* served in World War I in the Mediterranean. In the inter-war years she was used mostly as an aircraft transport or for trials. In World War II, by now renamed HMS *Pegasus*, she was used for a short period as a fighter-catapult ship, but was not finally scrapped until 1950.**

to protect aircraft from the elements and permit maintenance to be carried out; and handling gear, to transfer aircraft from the hangar to a position from which flying operations could be performed. Carrier development for the next fifty years would concern itself primarily with the refinement of these basic features. Other aspects of carrier aviation fully accepted today were also recognisable in 1913. For example, one of the aircraft carried by HMS *Hermes* on her manoeuvres was a Short S.64, which had folding wings to enable it to be stowed within the ship's stern hangar. Meanwhile, across the Atlantic, an aircraft had been successfully launched by compressed-air catapult in November 1912.

Even so, by the time war broke out in 1914 the role of the naval aircraft, and the value to the Fleet of the aircraft-carrying ship, was uncertain. The pre-war trials had demonstrated feasibilities but also pointed to problems. For example, aircraft could be launched and recovered only in relatively calm water; furthermore, co-ordination with the battle fleet was hampered both by the limited speeds of the carriers and the fact that they had to turn away into the wind, slow down or even stop altogether in order to operate their aircraft. Independent sorties seemed to be more appropriate.

One threat in particular exercised naval minds following the outbreak of hostilities: that posed by German Zeppelin airships, potentially highly efficient reconnaissance tools and purveyors of

Below: Spain's first carrier, *Dedalo* (10,800tons), a former merchant ship, was converted in 1922 to accommodate an airship, two balloons or two seaplanes. Her aircraft were used in action in the Riff wars in North Africa.

Below: 5am, 13 July 1918: German Zeppelin sheds at Tondern, Schleswig-Holstein on fire after an attack by seven Sopwith Camels launched from the carrier HMS *Furious*. Only three aircraft returned to the carrier.

destruction across the British mainland. Plans were swiftly drawn up by the Royal Navy to deal with the menace, thereby, almost at a stroke, introducing the concept of offensive and defensive action by ship-based aircraft in addition to their hitherto passive role of observation. A number of ships were requisitioned for conversion into seaplane carriers, and three of these, the ex-packets *Empress, Engadine* and *Riviera*, launched their aircraft on a bombing raid against the Zeppelin base at Cuxhaven. Though a failure in terms of tangible results, this pioneering effort laid the foundation for a doctrine that still bears relevance to this day – the projection of aerial strike power by means of ships. As the airship threat materialised, concern to combat this land-based bombing and reconnaissance force brought about a requirement to embark interceptor aircraft at sea. Float-equipped aircraft were at a disadvantage here, being generally too slow to make a successful rendezvous with their quarry, so adaptations of land-based fighters were introduced, held at readiness on bow ramps. In July 1916 a Bristol Scout landplane, armed with Ranken darts, rose from the carrier HMS *Vindex* (another converted steam packet) and successfully intercepted Zeppelin L17. Although the aircraft failed to bring the airship down, it was the first recorded instance of an aerial interception by a carrier-based fighter. In practice, however, such operations proved to be rare events, the one-way nature of the missions making normal commanders reluctant to sanction them.

The concept of the purpose-built carrier, capable of launching, recovering and stowing aircraft gradually evolved. Reflecting the uncertainties of the times, and the level of importance granted to aircraft-carrying ships, the First World War saw the introduction to service of a hotchpotch of carriers of vastly differing sizes, speeds and suitabilities. All were conversions of existing vessels, or at best modifications of existing designs. They included the conversions of the fast packets already mentioned (other examples being the British *Ben-my-Chree* and *Manxman* and the French *Nord* and *Pas-de-Calais*); of 3,000 to 3,500-ton (3,048 to 3,556 tonnes) mail steamers, such as the British *Pegasus* and *Nairana*; of 6,000 to 10,000-ton (6,096 to 10,160 tonnes) cargo ships like the German *Santa Elena*, the British *Ark Royal*, the Italian *Europa*, the Japanese *Wakamiya* and the Russian *Imperator Alexander I* and *Imperator Nikolai I*; and of a transatlantic passenger liner, the British *Campania*. Modifications worked into all these ships were limited, most of the original structure of the vessels being retained. Moreover, all were essentially seaplane carriers, recovery of their aircraft being effected by the latter landing alongside and then being hoisted on board by crane.

A number of important warship conversions were also put in hand during this period, none more so than the two affecting the large light cruiser HMS *Furious*, a graceful white elephant of a ship originally mounting a couple of monster 18in (47.5cm) guns. Her first refit saw the replacement of the forward turret with a

Left: This is the US Navy's fleet collier *Jupiter* (19,360tons), as commissioned in 1913. She was taken in hand and converted into the US Navy's first aircraft carrier, USS *Langley*, (as shown opposite) in 1920.

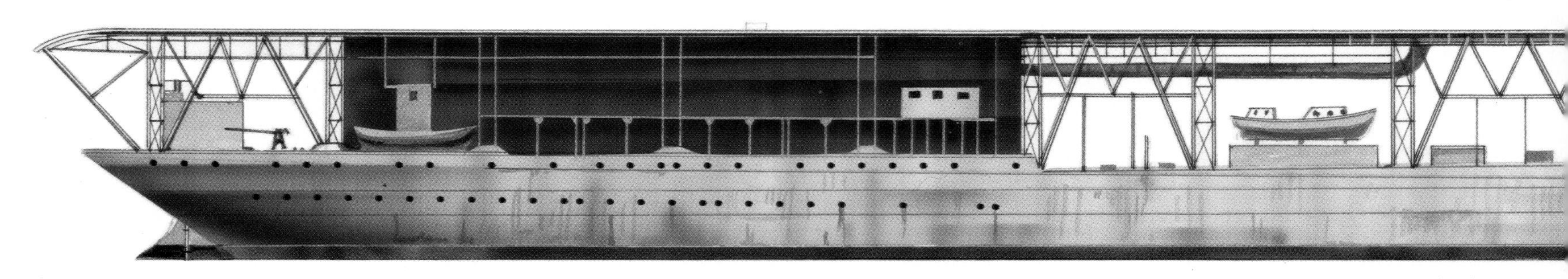

Right: A Sopwith Camel fighter taking-off from the seaplane carrier HMS *Pegasus* on 1 November 1918. Formerly the mail steamer *Stockholm*, *Pegasus* carried a total of 9 wheeled machines and seaplanes.

64ft 36ft (19.5m 10.7m) hangar and a 230ft (70m) flying-off deck, the ship's enormous forecastle being utilised to the maximum advantage. In this configuration HMS *Furious* hosted the first-ever deck landing by an aircraft on board a vessel under way, a feat performed in August 1917 by Sqn. Cdr. Dunning in a Sopwith Pup, who unfortunately perished a few days later while attempting the same manoeuvre. Subsequent trials led to the decision to refit HMS *Furious* further, her other 18in (47.5cm) turret and her mainmast being removed and a 280ft (85.4m) landing-on deck and a 70ft 38ft (21m 11.6m) hangar added, with lifts serving both hangars and gangways routed around the superstructure to allow aircraft to be wheeled forward for flying off. With a complement of sixteen machines, she was almost, but not quite, the prototype of the modern aircraft carrier.

Landing-on aboard HMS *Furious* proved to be the most perplexing problem facing carrier aviators. Indeed, very few operational landings were made on her after flight deck (and only ever once on the similarly configured HMS *Vindictive*, a converted 10,000-ton (10,160 tonnes) cruiser that was in effect a smaller edition of HMS *Furious*). It was only with the introduction into service in September 1918 of HMS *Argus*, a cargo liner rebuilt with

Above: The US Navy's first aircraft-carrier, USS *Langley* (CV-1), formerly the collier *Jupiter*, at anchor in the Canal Zone in 1930. The bridge was beneath the flight deck, leaving a clear area for aircraft operations.

Left: In 1937 *Langley* was converted into a seaplane-carrier and the forward part of the flight-deck was removed, leaving her as shown. She stayed in service until 1942, when she was sunk while being employed as an aircraft ferry.

Above: HMS *Furious* during World War II. Built as a cruiser in 1917 she was converted several times until she took on the flush-deck form shown here in the early 1920s. She served until being scrapped in 1948.

aircraft hangars topped by a full-length, unobstructed flight deck, that carrier aviation came of age. Had the First World War lasted a few more weeks, HMS *Argus* would have launched – and recovered – a squadron of Sopwith Cuckoo torpedo-bombers against the German fleet, thereby conducting the world's first mass air strike by shipboard aircraft.

Following the Armistice, and with the impetus to quickly commission further aircraft-carrying vessels removed, the development of the type, not surprisingly, slowed. The early-1920s saw the completion of the first purpose-designed aircraft carriers, Britain's HMS *Hermes* and Japan's IJN *Hosho*, and the Washington Treaty of 1922 provided the opportunity to convert a number of large ex-capital ship hulls into further carriers; the latter would form the nuclei of the carrier forces that later went to war in 1939 and 1941.

The ship-based aircraft, too, was developed, though with the immediacy of conflict supposedly removed the pace was, in general, leisurely. The role pioneered in the carrier raid on Cuxhaven and emulated in the attack on Tondern by aircraft from HMS *Furious* in July 1918 – that of striking land targets – was accorded a very low priority, and indeed all such independent operations were similarly relegated, particularly in the Royal Navy. Despite the absence of a major fleet action during the First World War (with the notable exception of that at Jutland), the big gun was still held to be the final arbiter in naval engagements, and all other "blue water" activities were subordinated to this doctrine. But perceptions changed, most noticeably in the US Navy.

Thus the roles of the naval aircraft evolved from what they had been in 1914–18; reconnaissance, to locate and observe enemy warships; spotting, to report on the accuracy of friendly gunfire (now even more important since engagements were beginning to be possible outside the visual range of the attacking ship, and becoming much more practicable with the development of radio equipment

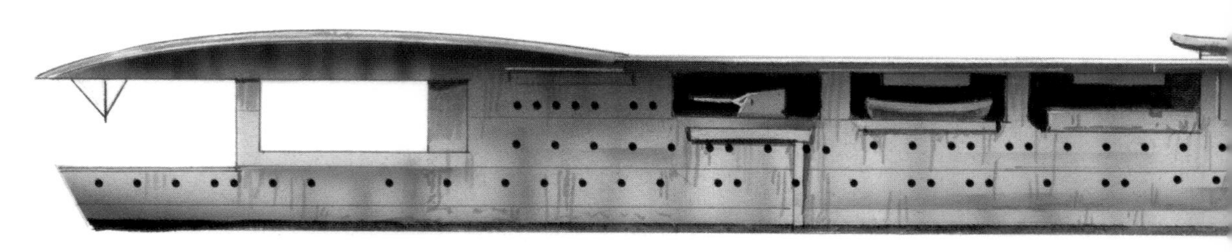

Right: HMS *Hermes* (13,000tons) was the first ship in any navy to be designed and built as an aircraft-carrier, all previous carriers having been conversions. However, she was small and had a very limited aircraft capacity — only 12 modern fighters in 1940. She was sunk by Japanese carrier aircraft off Ceylon, 9 April 1942.

compact enough to be taken aloft); and torpedo strike, to disable the enemy fleet once it had been found and its strength assessed. In addition, as in the First World War, fighter aircraft were employed, both to deny the enemy his reconnaissance facilities and to attack his strike aircraft; they might also be used against the enemy ships themselves, in a strafing and light bombing role. In most navies, in order to make more effective use of the space available on board ship, some of these roles were combined – hence the advent of the torpedo/spotter/reconnaissance aircraft (such as the Fairey Swordfish) in the Royal Navy and of the scout/dive-bomber (for example, the Curtiss SBC Helldiver) in the US Navy. Aircraft for interception and, later, spotting and reconnaissance were also embarked on board capital ships and heavy cruisers, and were carried aboard existing ships atop turret platforms and turret or quarterdeck catapults; from the 1930s on, enclosed hangars were frequently provided for these aircraft.

Above: Martin T4M torpedo-planes taking-off from USS *Lexington* (CV-2) in 1929. Converted from a battle-cruiser whilst on the stocks, she was commissioned in 1927. Note the huge stack and the eight 8in guns.

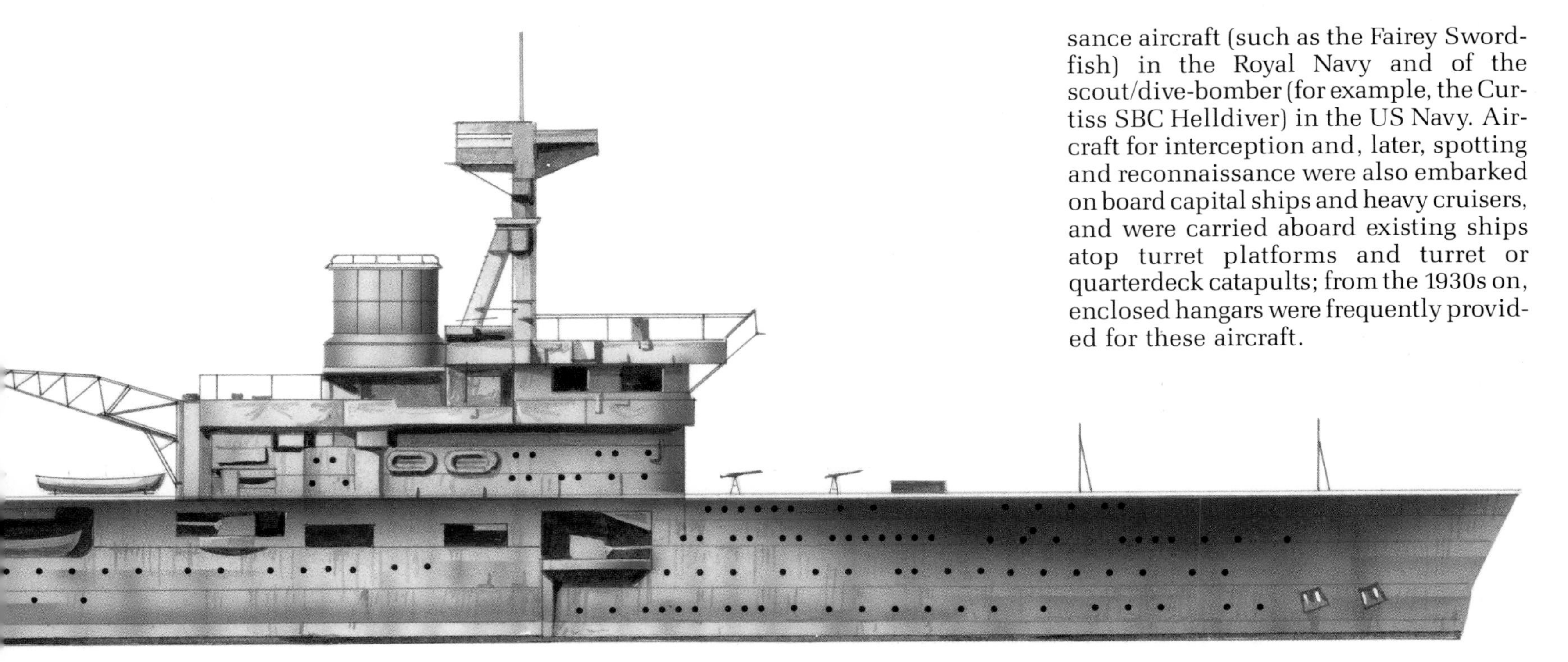

This doctrine persisted through to the late-1930s, particularly in the Royal Navy: in contrast, the US and Japanese navies (the only others with sizeable numbers of carriers at this time) began to explore the potential of the naval air strike force, envisaging attacks by carrier aircraft which could, independent of the battle fleet, sink enemy vessels. As luck would have it, two of the US capital ships on the slipways in 1922 were gigantic battlecruisers, lightly armoured and therefore potentially of very great capacity in relation to the tonnage limitations called for by the Washington Treaty. Such a complement (up to eighty aircraft), together with the policy of partially offloading fleet scout and observation aircraft to other types of ship, implied a formidable offensive capability. Gradually, through the 1930s, the concept of a coherent Air Group evolved. So did that of a Carrier Task Force – that is, a group composed of different types of ships with an aircraft carrier at its core, mutually protective, and sailing and operating independently of the main battle fleet. The seeds of the demise of the traditional capital ship were thereby sown. The Task Force, capable of speeds several knots faster than the battle line, could bring to bear enough offensive power to enable it to dispose of enemy capital ships; assuming that the enemy carriers might be able to do the same thing, the implication was that the big-gun ship might perhaps become sidelined – irrelevant almost.

Although it embraced the fighter aircraft, the scout/observation aircraft and the torpedo-bomber, US Navy carrier doctrine placed great faith in the dive-bomber, doubtless influenced by the demonstration in 1921 by Brigadier-General Billy Mitchell of the aerial bombardment and sinking of the ex-enemy battleship *Ostfriesland*; trials suggested that dive-bombing was a more effective way of disabling a ship than launching

Left: USS *Saratoga* (CV-3) in 1929-30. Like *Lexington* she could carry some 80 aircraft, including the Boeing F3B-1 fighters (forward) and Martin T4M-1 torpedo bombers (aft) seen here preparing for take-off.

airborne torpedoes at it, and many times more accurate than level bombing. The first US aircraft carrier actually to be designed as such, the USS *Ranger* of 1933, made no provision at all for torpedo bombers (although the type would re-emerge as a potent US Navy weapon in the

Right: On early carriers longitudinal wires kept aircraft straight, but they stopped by hooking transverse wires.

Below: US Navy Martin T4M with hook extended flies over *Lexington*.

Left: The concept of carrier task groups was being tested in the early 1930s, as shown in this splendid shot of *Saratoga*, *Lexington* and *Ranger*, operating in the Pacific. The aircraft are Boeing F4B pursuit fighters.

Second World War). Thus a typical USN Air Group of the mid-1930s comprised two squadrons of fighters (which could carry a limited bomb load), two squadrons of scout/dive-bombers and a few miscellaneous aircraft (those used for observation and liaison etc.).

The Royal Navy emphasised torpedo attack and throughout the 1920s and 1930s (and, indeed, during the Second World War) operated a succession of Sopwith, Blackburn and Fairey types, most of which could, optionally, carry bombs. It had no dedicated level bombers during this period, nor a dive-bomber until the advent in 1938-39 of the Blackburn Skua (which was in reality a fighter with a secondary dive-bombing capability). The function of the British carrier was different from that of its US counterpart: it was still seen as an adjunct of the battle fleet, hence would be pitted directly against enemy battle fleets. Moreover, torpedo attack was considered far more likely to achieve results than bombing – at the very least, such a tactic could slow battleships down, enabling friendly capital ships to finish the job. The pursuit and sinking of the German battleship *Bismarck* in the spring of 1941 is often cited as a classic Fleet Air Arm action; according to the Royal Navy doctrine of the day, it was exactly that.

Left Centre: One of the most splendid of all carrier operations was the 'Doolittle Raid' against Japan. Here one of the sixteen B-25s climbs steeply away from the flight-deck of USS *Hornet* (CV-8) on 18 April 1942.

Left: Swordfish torpedo bombers fly over HMS *Ark Royal* (22,000tons) just before the outbreak of World War II. *Ark Royal* had a great reputation, but was sunk by a torpedo from a German submarine on 13 November 1941.

Above: During World War II most US Navy battleships mounted at least one aircraft catapult on the fantail, together with a large crane. These were used to launch and recover floatplanes, like this Vought OS2U on board USS *Iowa* in 1943.

Nevertheless, six months before the *Bismarck* action the Fleet Air Arm had delivered a severe blow to the Italian Fleet at Taranto by launching a crippling aerial torpedo attack using carrier-based Swordfishes. This was the first true demonstration under wartime conditions of the power projection concept, which would become a central theme of post-war carrier doctrine and is still such today. At Taranto there was never any question of following up the airborne attack with heavy gunfire: the carrier operation was an end in itself. In retrospect it appears that the profound implications of this highly successful action were not fully appreciated, at least not in British circles.

Fleet Air Arm fighters were more of a problem. The task of the fighter was seen essentially as being one of escort; on the high seas, assuming a European foe, there would be few aircraft to intercept since enemy carriers hardly existed. The single-seat fighter disappeared and the type was assigned secondary roles – light bombing, dive-bombing and reconnaissance. Moreover, since the aircraft were to accompany the strike force, out of visible range of the parent ship, an observer/navigator would be required. Fleet air defence by fighter aircraft was not needed: fixed anti-aircraft guns could look after that, and thus the penalties imposed on aircraft speed and agility by the second seat were of little consequence. Later, during the Second World War, when British carriers had to operate under threat from land-based enemy aircraft, the air defence fighter was seen as a vital component of the Air Group and some quick re-thinking was called for.

The Imperial Japanese Navy of the interwar years at first embraced a tactical doctrine similar to that of the the Royal Navy, perhaps not surprisingly in view of the Anglo-Japanese alliance that existed during the First World War and the considerable assistance rendered in Japanese carrier design, and in carrier aircraft design, by the British during the 1920s. It became apparent, however, that Japan's most likely opponent in any future conflict would be the United States, and during the 1930s this perceived threat was addressed with some urgency. Torpedo-bombers and fighter aircraft were retained, but a new dive-

Left: 7 December 1941 and a torpedo-carrying Nakajima B5N 'Kate' takes off from a Japanese aircraft carrier heading for Pearl Harbor and one of the most devastating air strikes in naval history.

bomber was developed (culminating in the famous Aichi D1A1 ''Val'') and faith was kept with level bombing; meanwhile reconnaissance and spotting were delegated to seaplanes operating off cruisers, apparently confirming the view that the carrier now was a tool of attack in its own right and had no role acting as the eyes of the gunners.

The theory was put into practice in the pre-emptive attack on Pearl Harbor on 7 December 1941, when virtually the entire battleship force of the US Pacific Fleet was put out of action by a combination of torpedo-bombing, dive-bombing and level bombing, in two attack waves flown off six carriers. It is often said that the outcome of the British attack at Taranto in November 1940 profoundly influenced Japanese decisions concerning Pearl Harbor. However, while the effects were repeated on a larger scale, the methods used were significantly different: half the torpedo-bombers flown in the first wave were armed with adapted naval armour-piercing shells and all of them in the second wave were so armed. Altogether, only 15 per cent of the individual attacks were carried out using torpedoes; compared with 47 per cent by dive-bombing and 38 per cent by level bombing.

It was the US Navy's great good fortune that none of its aircraft carriers were present at Pearl Harbor that day: now there could be no question of a big-gun fleet action, even if one had been anticipated. The power projection demonstrated by the Japanese was a stunning vindication of the pro-carrier lobby's views. Even so, an airborne attack against a manoeuvring target on the high seas was not quite the same as one against a line of ships in harbour. However, the Japanese appeared to have no problems: three days after Pearl Harbor their land-based bombers sank the British capital ships HMS *Repulse* and *Prince of Wales*, the latter virtually a brand new battleship equipped with what were considered to be the last word in anti-aircraft defences.

Events in the Pacific from 1942 brought about rapid and far-reaching changes in the operation of aircraft at sea, and within months of the outbreak of war between Japan and the United States it was clearly understood that combat between the major elements of the two countries' navies would take place not at long distances apart across the surface of the water that separated them, but high in the skies above, frequently far away from the parent ships. Thus the key to the mastery of the seas – specifically, the Pacific Ocean – lay with aircraft carriers, not big-gun battleships. Aircraft now carried bombs and torpedoes substituted for shells, the main armament being, as it were, sent aloft on an aircraft and directed visually and individually to its target. The offensive reach of the opposing navies thereby increased to previously unheard-of distances.

The Second World War fully vindicated the United States' pre-war carrier doctrine, given the kind of naval campaign that unfolded. Air power was the overwhelming requirement, not only in order to amass strike aircraft in sufficient numbers to defeat enemy naval air power (i.e. its carriers), but also to amass sufficient fighters to defeat the enemy's defen-

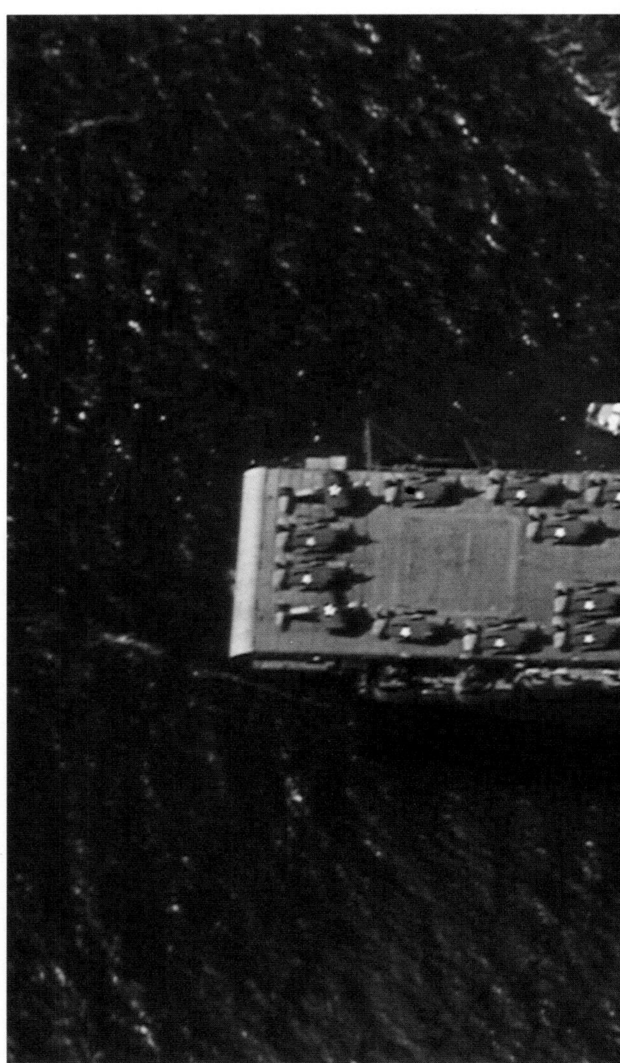

ding aircraft and thus enable the strike to succeed; conversely, enough fighters had to be retained in order to deny the enemy access to one's own ship. The first Pacific carrier battle, at Coral Sea in May 1942, was close-run, but after the US victory at Midway the following month, when four large Japanese carriers were sunk, American industry supplied ships and aircraft in such numbers, and with such rapidity, that the Japanese were never able to regain the advantage.

Air Group composition at this time had been modified from that evident in the 1930s, as much to reflect the handling capacities of the ships as any major change in tactical procedure. Thus at the oubreak of war USS *Hornet* accommodated one squadron of fighters (VF-8: Grumman F4F Wildcats), one of torpedo-bombers (VT-8: Douglas TBD Devastators) and two of scout/dive-bombers (VB-8 and VS-8: Curtiss SBC-4 Helldivers, in practice conducting the two missions separately), each with a nominal strength of eighteen aircraft. Three years later the wartime complement of her sister ship USS *Enterprise* was little changed, although an extra squadron of fighters (Grumman F6F Hellcats) had been taken aboard. The torpedo-bombers were now Grumman TBF Avengers and the scout/dive-bombers Douglas SBD Dauntlesses. As the number of carrier hulls multiplied, and as light fleet carriers and escort carriers became available to supplement the big fleet carriers, so a degree of specialisation was introduced. Hence escort carriers generally did not embark scout/ dive-bombers towards the end of the war, preferring one squadron each of fighters and torpedo-bombers.

In the Royal Navy from 1941 on, Air Group composition started to become fighter-heavy, primarily in response to experience gained in the Mediterranean theatre of operations, where carriers were repeatedly subjected to fierce attacks from land-based Axis aircraft. Air defence constituted a role of ever-growing importance, but at first specialised aircraft to fulfil such tasks were unavailable. Developments (Fairey Fulmar) and conversions (Supermarine Seafire, Hawker Sea Hurricane) of existing land-based aircraft were

Below: The design of the USS *Wasp* (CV-7) was limited by the Washington Treaty and protection against torpedoes was omitted. Severely damaged by a Japanese submarine in 1942, she had to be sunk.

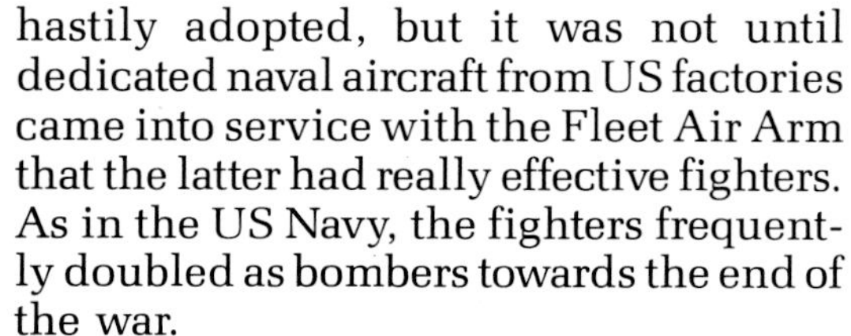

hastily adopted, but it was not until dedicated naval aircraft from US factories came into service with the Fleet Air Arm that the latter had really effective fighters. As in the US Navy, the fighters frequently doubled as bombers towards the end of the war.

With the destruction of the Japanese fleet and the coming of peace, the United States was left with an enormous force of aircraft carriers, and Great Britain with a small but not insignificant one, but there was no carrier fleet against which they

Above: Ensign Ardon R. Ives, USN makes a rapid exit from his burning Grumman F6F Hellcat after a spectacular landing aboard USS *Lexington* (CV-16). 12,272 F6Fs were built in total.

Below: US Navy fighters eventually dominated their Japanese counterparts. Commander David McCampbell, personally destroyed over 30 Japanese aircraft in air-to-air combat.

might have to be pitched in the immediate post-war years; in fact, with one exception, there was no foreseeable naval threat at all. The one problem, which might become acute in due course, was the large submarine fleet belonging to the Soviet Union. While the dangers posed by U-boats had, by the end of the war, more or less been contained (thanks largely to radar-equipped aircraft), it was widely appreciated that new German submarines, of high underwater speed and long endurance, could have made a very great impact had the conflict lasted longer. In the post-war years, it was known that the technology behind these boats was available to the Soviet Union and being incorporated into their designs.

Accordingly, anti-submarine warfare (ASW), demanding specialist aircraft, was a prominent theme of post-war US naval policy. So seriously was the problem taken that first war-built escort carriers and then *Essex* class fleet carriers were refitted to enable them to operate purely in an ASW role. Originally, the requirement to lift air-to-surface vessel (ASV) radar equiment and attack weapons, and to ensure a long loiter capability to search for targets, necessitated two aircraft per sortie, operating as a hunter/killer pair; the first

Below: The McDonnell F-3H-1 Demon was one of the most effective naval jet fighters of the late 1950s. This aircraft is about to be launched by the newly-installed steam-catapult on USS *Roosevelt* (CVA-42).

Left: The US Navy's carrier-based ASW requirements during the 1950s were satisfied by a hunter-killer team comprising the Grumman AF-2W Guardian (nearest) and the armed AF-2S Guardian respectively.

US dedicated ASW aircraft were the Grumman AF-2W (radar platform) and AF-2S Guardian (strike) pair. Later the twin-engined Grumman S2F Tracker was developed, combining all the requirements of airborne ASW in one airframe, its large size quite acceptable when the larger converted fleet carriers re-entered service.

However, ASW was not the US carrier fleet's primary concern. The Soviet Union – in 1945 perceived as the only potential enemy of the US – was essentially a great land power and, in the face of US Air Force (USAF) opposition, the Navy addressed this fact in its own inimitable way, championing the role of the aircraft carrier as a strategic strike weapon. Given a large enough aircraft, and a large enough ship from which to operate it, virtually the entire land mass of the Soviet Union could be brought within strike range. Such an aircraft might also, of course, carry an atomic bomb (then considered unlikely to be less than 10,000lb (4,540kg) in weight). This was the rationale behind the laying down of the first post-war carrier, the USS *United States*. Existing fleet carriers, the largest of which were the new Midway class vessels, could conduct strategic warfare at an interim range, operating the mixed-power North American AJ Savage bomber then under development. Budget constraints (and, probably, vigorous lobbying by the USAF), brought about the cancellation of the USS *United States*, and the Navy had to make do with its interim aircraft, replaced later by the all-jet Douglas A3D Skywarrior. The latter, with a gross weight of some 70,000lb (31,780kg) was the aircraft the new *Forrestal* class super carriers of

Below: Bigger and better than the Guardian, Grumman's S2F Tracker combined the hunter-killer tasks in one ASW platform. Illustrated are Brazilian examples, warming up aboard the carrier *Minas Gerais*.

Right: A typical scene aboard a US Navy carrier during the 1960s, in this case the USS *Oriskany* (CV-34), with the large size of two A3D Skywarriors in sharp contrast to the smaller Skyhawks and Crusaders.

1950 were designed to operate; in fact, to a large extent it determined the ships' general layout and dimensions.

Other considerations drove up the size of the new post-war carriers, not the least being the proliferation of new roles for the aircraft they embarked. Even during the latter stages of the Second World War, competition for deck space intensified with the requirement for specialized photo-reconnaissance aircraft and night fighters (usually adapted F6F Hellcats). A small ASW detachment was still thought desirable, even though the main burden was now to be borne by the former escort carriers; the prospect of aerial refuelling, giving existing aircraft far greater ranges, implied the embarkation of specialized tanker aircraft. The quest for greater range brought about increased aircraft size: thus the successor to the single-engined escort fighters was the twin-engined Grumman F7F Tigercat. Conversely, the installation of shipboard long-range radar systems reduced the need to rely on scout aircraft, at least for defensive reconnaissance.

British carrier policy in the immediate post-war years was less flamboyant. The surviving pre-war carriers – of First World War origin, of course – were worn out, the Lend-Lease escort carriers had to be returned to the United States, and there remained the half-dozen *Illustrious*-type ships and a number of light fleet carriers. New fleet carriers were under construction, but post-war austerity and the need to reassess technological, military and political requirements meant that no clear-cut decision as to their future was arrived at and the tempo of building slackened; for example, the 45,000-ton (45,720 tonnes) HMS *Eagle*, laid down in 1942, was not commissioned until 1951.

In fact, for ten years after the end of the Second World War, carrier aviation was thrown into confusion. The cause was the introduction of the jet aircraft. In

033

Previous Page: Seemingly straining at the leash, a Blackburn Buccaneer of No. 809 Squadron awaits the pull of the catapult aboard the Royal Navy's carrier HMS *Ark Royal*.

particular, the relatively poor acceleration of a jet off the deck and its high landing speed seemed to compromise the slick operating procedures that had been perfected during the war. These concerns, together with other problems such as the need to stow a different type of aviation fuel on board ship and the poor fuel consumption (hence limited range) of the early jets, brought about a thoroughgoing reassessment of carrier characteristics. For a considerable period, nevertheless, jet and piston-engined aircraft operated side by side; indeed, it was not until the S2F Tracker was replaced by the Lockheed S-3 Viking in the mid-1970s that the US Navy finally abandoned piston-engined carrier aircraft.

The first carrier jets were wartime designs; unsurprisingly, given their improved speeds and high fuel consumption, they were all small fighters (and thus doubled as light bombers), scarcely suitable for the long-range attack mission. The first deck landing by a jet aircraft took place in December 1945 using a tiny de Havilland Vampire. This type did not pass into service, the Fleet Air Arm preferring to introduce an entirely new design, the tail-sitting Supermarine Attacker, and subsequently the more advanced Armstrong-Whitworth Sea Hawk. Greater choice was available to the US Navy, and three first-generation naval jet fighters – the McDonnell FH Phantom, North American FJ Fury and McDonnell F2H Banshee – equipped front-line squadrons. All were straight-winged aircraft, as were the first generation of jet night-fighters, the US Douglas F3D Skyknight and the British de Havilland Sea Venom. With the refining of airborne radar systems during the 1950s and 1960s, the all-weather interceptor superseded the day fighter and rendered a separate night fighter superfluous, while the multi-role fighter, still able to carry bombs, became the standard carrier aircraft of its type. Strike escort and carrier (Task Force) air defence were still the primary roles of the fighter; the latter conducted by a combination of combat air patrol (CAP) and deck-launched interception (DLI). In CAP, aircraft maintained a constant vigil at distances of 100 to 150 miles (170 to 241km) from the parent ship, watching for, and attacking if necessary, enemy airborne threats; in DLI, up to two fighters were held at readiness on catapults, to be launched against a threat once detected. The DLI concept did not survive for long as an air defence technique, although it was still considered relevant in the French post-war carrier force (which lacked an airborne early warning (AEW) capability).

Gradually, the modern Carrier Air Group developed. The phasing out of the specialist ASW carriers in the mid-1960s transferred the fleet ASW role to the big attack carriers, and anti-submarine

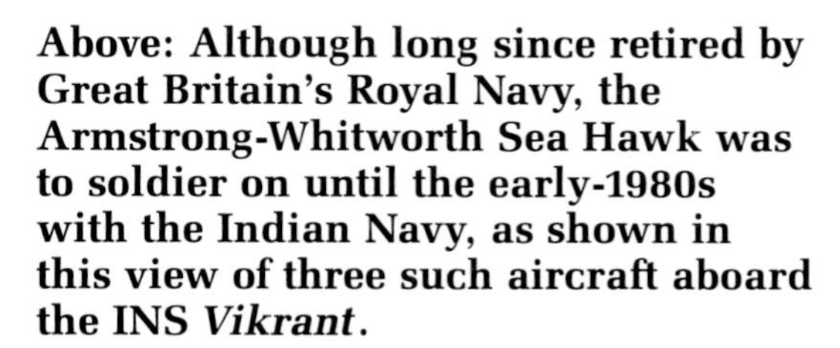

Above: Although long since retired by Great Britain's Royal Navy, the Armstrong-Whitworth Sea Hawk was to soldier on until the early-1980s with the Indian Navy, as shown in this view of three such aircraft aboard the INS *Vikrant*.

Left: The decommissioning of HMS *Ark Royal* in 1979 left the Royal Navy without a credible Air Group at sea – an asset that was to be sorely missed three years later when the Falklands War broke out.

aircraft now found themselves jostling for space with not only fighters and strike aircraft, but also the other specialist models; at first tankers, then AEW and electronic countermeasures (ECM) machines. The torpedo-bomber and the scout/dive-bomber disappeared soon after the war with the advent of practicable air-to-surface guided missiles (the torpedo being retained as an anti-submarine weapon, carried by dedicated ASW aircraft).

Royal Navy post-war carrier policy by and large echoed US doctrine, albeit in miniature form. There was little pretence, however, at endowing the aircraft carriers with a strategic role; quite apart from the expense, the ships were simply not large enough to sustain a long-range nuclear bombing capability. However, aircraft designers produced a succession of rugged, powerful naval machines, culminating in the superlative Blackburn Buccaneer which, once equipped with economical turbofan engines, was arguably the finest carrier-borne strike aircraft ever produced. The British abandonment of the fleet carrier, signalled finally with the decommissioning of HMS *Ark Royal* in 1979, was an acknowledgement that the cost of maintaining a credible, cohesive Air Group at sea was beyond what the politicians of the day were prepared to countenance. Whether the decision was a wise one is another matter. Other opportunities were presented, however, with the arrival on the scene of a viable vertical/short take-off and landing (V/STOL) aircraft in the form of the Hawker-Siddeley Harrier: now jet fighters could be taken to sea without the need for an enormous flight deck, implying small ships (though also limited capacity) and hence low cost. Two ex-British wartime light fleet carriers are currently operated by the Indian Navy in this way, and US amphibious assault ships also embark V/STOL aircraft as part of their air component; but the Royal Navy's three Invincible class carriers are the primary exponents of this form of naval air warfare. Ostensibly anti-submarine carriers, they are also capable of operating as strike carriers in a limited fashion – and indeed as assault ships. Their value, though much diminished in comparison with the enormous US Navy fleet carriers (and even with the last Royal Navy fleet carriers), has been amply demonstrated as shown in the 1982 Falklands War.

Below: Now the sole fixed-wing aircraft operating from the Royal Navy's trio of Invicible class light aircraft carriers, the BAe Sea Harrier is the *raison d'etre* for the highly distinctive 12° ''ski jump'' take-off ramp at the bow.

2

Taking Shape

THERE is no such thing as an ideal aircraft carrier. Like all ships, the carrier is a compromise of conflicting requirements, and all that can be asked of a carrier designer is that he come up with a ship that performs each of its tasks in the least unfavourable fashion. The demands of the customer – that is, the Navy – are great, but rarely can all be met, and as well as having to decide which ideals have to be sacrificed the designer is frequently constrained within political guidelines, not the least of which is cost. In the case of carriers, the task is further complicated in that their main armament – in other words their aircraft – has to be integrated into the ships, and aircraft manufacturers do not in general design the ships from which their products operate. Furthermore, carriers today represent so great a capital investment that they are expected, reasonably, to be capable of remaining in service over several decades, and although a carrier may be refitted and modernized at stages during its career, it cannot be fundamentally altered within a reasonable budget. Aircraft rarely enjoy such longevity. Thus from the outset the carrier designer is limited by aircraft technology, and has to speculate intelligently about the advances in naval aircraft design and capability that *might* occur in the future. Eventually, however, it is the aircraft designer who must compromise, having to ensure that his products are compatible with those carriers currently in being.

Such integration of thought could hardly be expected to occur during the pioneering years. With little real concept of what could reasonably be achieved by shipboard aircraft, and with only a vague notion of what their roles might be – there was, after all, precious little experience to draw on – those responsible for the early seaplane carriers were very much pioneers of their day. In retrospect, it is remarkable that so much was accomplished in terms of carrier development during the four years of the First World War: the transition from barely-modified steamers and cargo ships to fully-fledged aircraft carriers whose general appearance, equipment and operating procedures are still evident in today's fleets was achieved extraordinarily quickly.

Below: Despite the relatively wide landing-on deck clearly visible in this view, the battleship origins of HMS *Furious* are easy to see in the shape of her long, slender bow and the location of the superstructure amidships. Positioned to the aft of the landing-on deck is one of the two hangar access points.

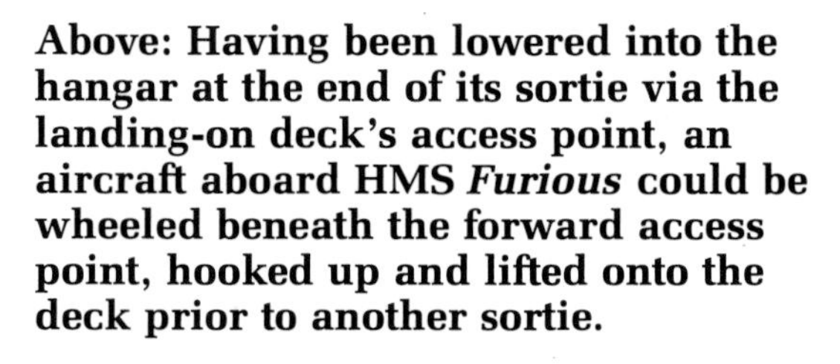

Above: Having been lowered into the hangar at the end of its sortie via the landing-on deck's access point, an aircraft aboard HMS *Furious* could be wheeled beneath the forward access point, hooked up and lifted onto the deck prior to another sortie.

Above: Caught by the camera in 1924, a Vought UO-1 floatplane skims the waves as it passes the vast bulk of USS *Langley* (CV-1), the US Navy's first aircraft carrier. Floatplanes would often land alongside a carrier and be hoisted aboard for relaunch.

Below: With space at a premium, any means by which an aircraft's size can be lessened, especially when in the hangar, is a welcome bonus. In the main, such attempts concentrate on reducing the wing span, as shown to good effect on this A-6 Intruder.

Although the modern carrier exists to operate aircraft, this is only the most important consideration among a wide range that the designer has to take into account. Thus not only does it have to make provision for the launch and recovery of aircraft, it also has to provide hangarage, repair and maintenance facilities for them. It also has to store the ordnance they require, and their fuel and spares, and it has to accommodate and feed the air crews, deck crews and maintenance crews. The carrier is also mobile, hence it has to accommodate its own powerplant and fuel, and its own services (for example, water supply and electricity); and will also most probably have its own fixed armament, which must be served, maintained and manned (a particular concern in the past when carriers were equipped with very powerful shipboard gun batteries). Finally, there are all

Right: Primary targets for Japanese *kamikaze* attacks were US aircraft carriers. Here USS *Belleau Wood* (CVL-24) blazes on 30 October 1944, with crewmen fighting to save as many Grumman TBF Avengers as possible.

the traditional requirements of running a warship, the reductions in manpower achieved post- war by means of automation and other labour-saving measures to some extent offset nowadays by the increased specialisations (for example, electronics) called for in modern naval warfare.

The hull of the aircraft carrier differs form that of other types of warship in a number of respects. For example, since a carrier's superstructure is minimal, the hull has to accommodate what might otherwise be sited top-side. Additionally, the hull has to provide a very stable platform in order to facilitate aircraft operations: the pitching and rolling that might have been acceptable in a Second World War destroyer is undesirable in a carrier. This is one argument in favour of the carrier having a large hull. Put crudely, rolling is influenced by hull form (i.e. the shape of its cross-section) and pitching by ship length (the longer the hull, the less it will be affected by wave action). Moreover, the larger the hull the higher the permissible freeboard for a given form. One reason why the bow ramps of the First World War seaplane carriers were so rarely used is that sea states, drenching the forecastle, precluded such launches.

The size of the hull also influences the ship's range: the greater the amount of fuel carried, the further the ship might travel; the greater the tonnage of onboard provisions, the longer it can last without replenishment; and the more ordnance that can be embarked, the more aircraft sorties can be flown (i.e. the faster the strike rate or, alternatively, the longer the

Right: British carriers had armoured flightdecks, US carriers did not. As a result *kamikaze* attacks could penetrate into the hangar, as here on USS *Intrepid* (CV-11).

ship can remain on station before having its stocks replenished). Generally, in the past, range was largely determined by bunkerage capacity; nowadays, in nuclear carriers, which can steam for months on end without refuelling, range, or rather endurance, is to a large extent determined by such factors as ordnance capacity or even human fatigue. This is why a small nuclear-powered carrier is regarded by many as an absurdity: there is very little point in building a carrier with a range of 500,000 miles, if she requires stores and ordnance replishment every 10,000. Conversely, given the great endurance conferred (and cost incurred) by a nuclear powerplant, the temptation to endow such a ship with an enormous self-sustaining capacity is irresistible.

However, all this equipment cannot be merely crammed in; it has to be protected, ensuring at the very least that a single hit will not disable the ship. (Here again is an argument in favour of very large carriers: their sheer size reduces the likelihood that a single hit will cause terminal damage since the damaged area will probably affect a smaller fraction of the hull than it would in a smaller ship.) A variety of systems are employed, some obvious, some subtle – and some, in a modern carrier, classified. For example, a good degree of self-protection can be achieved merely by the intelligent use of space. Thus if propulsion units are spread out instead of being concentrated in one area of the hull, one hit will be unlikely to cause complete immobilization; similarly, if the ammunition magazines are spaced out, one hit will probably not bring about the total loss of the ship, especially if the magazines are placed below the waterline. However, at least in conventionally-powered carriers, the machinery needs to be close to the uptakes and funnels, which influences the postion of the island superstructure and hence affects flight deck layout.

Further protection is achieved in more traditional ways. A complex system of subdivision, enforced by watertight bulkheads, ensures that, in the event of water ingress as a result of an underwater hit, flooding can be localised, and counter-flooding on the opposite side of the hull will help to correct any list. Torpedo bulkheads, enclosing compartments containing fuel oil (ship fuel in a conventional carrier, slow-burning aviation kerosene in a nuclear carrier), are still an effective measure, capable of absorbing shock and thereby dissipating the force of an explosion. Armour plate is also still a valid protective system, distributed internally, in limited form, around such vitals as machinery and magazines (and, presumably, reactor plants).

Central to the theme of hull design is the question of its overall strength. In contrast to British practice, US wartime carriers (the *Yorktowns* and *Essexes*) had their hulls enclosed by the hangar deck, the hangers themselves forming a comparatively lightweight structure topped by a flight deck which was not in itself a strength deck. British carrier designers, on the other hand, used the flight deck as a strength deck; thus, in effect, the aircraft hangars were enclosed within the hull, their sides forming a significant aspect of the internal hull structure. However, given the enormous size of the post-war US carriers, the stresses on the hull imposed by rough weather etc. demanded a deepening of its structure, and the flight deck, now having to accept ever-increasing aircraft weights also, had to be incorporated as part of the hull proper.

The prototypes of the pre-First World War and early war years, being hastily arranged conversions of existing ships, did not enjoy the luxury of a complete,

Below: Cross-section through a typical British World War II carrier, showing the engine room, uptake trunking, hangar and flightdeck. The hangar was an armoured box, which contributed greatly to the overall strength of the hull. The armour plating on the hull sides was 3.5in (89mm) thick.

studied design process: they concerned themselves purely with the launch and recovery of aircraft, incorporating also some basic protection for the latter against the elements. However, some effort was usually made to give the converted merchantmen a measure of self-protection in the form of a few guns; thus, for example, the fast packets generally had 12pdr and 3pdr guns added, for defence against surface and airborne threats respectively, and HMS *Argus*, a more radical conversion (and a considerably larger ship), received half a dozen 4in (10cm) guns, four of them for high-angle fire.

The provision of a fixed armament has historically been a perplexing question. Most carriers of the inter-war period were originally equipped with medium-calibre guns of varying profusion, generally because it was felt desirable that they should be able to cope with a surprise attack by enemy ships. The scouting role of the carriers implied that the main problem was likely to be enemy scouts (i.e. cruisers), and so a cruiser-type armament was considered appropriate; for this reason also, cruiser-type armour belt protection was usually adopted. Thus the British *Eagle* of 1924 (laid down as a battleship) retained her designed 6in (15cm) secondary armament (which equated approximately to a cruiser's main battery) and had her armour belt reduced in thickness from 9in (23cm) maximum to 4in (11.4cm) maximum.

As the air threat became more apparent during the inter-war years, and as the task force concept began to be adopted, the fixed surface battery fell into disfavour: it did, after all, consume considerable weight if not space, and the chances of a surface engagement, given the high carrier speeds of the day, seemed ever more remote; moreover, surface defence could conveniently be delegated to other ships in the task force and, perhaps, the threat could also be addressed by embarking more fighter aircraft. There remained, however, the possibility of enemy aircraft getting through, possibly when the carrier's own air assets were themselves

Above: A World War II Essex class carrier shows two quad 40mm mounts (nearest the camera), two twin 5in (127mm) turrets, a battery of ten 20mm cannon in a long sponson, with another two 'quad-40s' below and, aft, yet another quad 40mm.

Right: USS *Lexington* (CV-2) as she was when sunk on 8 May 1942. She was originally armed with eight 8in (203mm) guns (see page 15), but these were removed in early 1942. The planned twin 5in (127mm) DP replacements had not been fitted by the time she was lost, at the battle of the Coral Sea.

engaged in a distant attack. Anti-aircraft guns therefore began to proliferate, culminating in vast numbers of barrels appearing towards the end of the Second World War. Well over a hundred 0.8in (20mm) and 1.6in (40mm) guns was not untypical (and, of course, caused conditions on board to become exceedingly cramped). Medium-calibre guns have now all but disappeared from carriers – the manpower they require and the weight they eat up can more usefully be employed elsewhere – although a few light-rapid-fire AA weapons and surface-to-air missile (SAM) launchers are generally retained, as an insurance against an attacking aircraft not being caught before coming within range.

It is in its aircraft arrangements that the carrier differs so markedly from other types of warship. Its silhouette is unmistakable, and while the internal arrangements may not visibly advertise the ship's role, its external configuration most decidedly does. This defining shape was not originally so obvious, however, nor did it evolve without considerable research and experimentation. In the pioneering days, the choice of vessels available for conversion was extremely limited: front-line warships were required for the purpose for which they were originally intended, and merchant ships were needed to support the war effort, either as cargo vessels or troop transports.

Above: Today's equivalent of the 40mm cannon is the Vulcan/Phalanx 20mm Close-in Weapon System (CIWS), seen here with a gunner's mate inspecting the ammunition carriage system. The seven barrels have a cyclic rate of fire of 3,000 rounds per minute.

Left: The Washington Naval Treaty defined aircraft carriers as "warships designed expressly to carry aircraft". This 17,500ton Japanese design was a 1932 attempt to evade such provisions by declaring the ship to be a cruiser (hence the 6 x 8in (203mm) guns) which just happened to have a flight deck attached! It was never built.

Above: Having been hoisted out of the hangar via the forward access point, a trio of Royal Naval Air Service Sopwith Camels prepare to launch from HMS *Furious*. Note the fold-down windbreaks, protecting the aircraft from air turbulence.

Above: Although Great Britain and the United States led the way in carrier-borne experimentation, the French were also learning fast. In this 1920 photograph, a Nieuport 17 leaves the sloop *Bapaume*.

Moreover, the emergency of the time most likely precluded any complex and time-consuming conversion work: effective carriers, given that they were a valid requirement, were needed quickly. This explains why the first Royal Navy carriers were adapted from, among others, cross-channel packets, mail steamers and a condemned passenger liner.

Thus to a large extent the operational deployment of these ships was limited by the original characteristics of the vessels concerned. For example, the shape and size of the hull were fixed, as were the machinery and accommodation inside. All aviation-related activities, therefore, had to be conducted topside, and conversion work was generally confined to clearing quarterdecks, adding handling derricks if necessary, carrying out some minor modifications to the superstructure, fitting a ramp over the forecastle, adding some canvas screening to protect the aircraft (subsequently improved by substituting a rigid hangar) and, later, bolting down some gun mountings; the modifications to HMS *Engadine*, one of the first packets to be adapted, took precisely 21 days. As a result, aircraft complements were tiny: a carrier with four such machines on board was considered to be well equipped.

One exception to this work pattern concerned a collier/grain carrier, *Konakry*, in frame at Blyth, Northumberland, in early 1914. Purchased by the Admiralty, the ship had her internal arrangements extensively redesigned to incorporate a large hangar with a sliding hatch, through which aircraft could be hoisted. Her machinery was shifted right aft, to make room for the hangar, and a long, flat forecastle served as a take-off deck (though in practice it would rarely be used as such). The ship was renamed HMS *Ark Royal*, and this vessel is often described as the world's first true aircraft carrier.

Clearly, the stowage of aircraft below deck necessitated some means to raise

Right: Another example of a cruiser converted into an aircraft carrier, HMS *Courageous* was unusual in that she was fitted with an additional take-off deck some 60ft (18.30m) in length, permitting landing and take-off at the same time.

them to a take-off position, and a flat deck forward to enable them to fly off represented a considerable advance; moreover, aircraft capacity increased (HMS *Ark Royal* could accommodate up to twelve of them), and the problem of excessive topweight, another limiting factor in ''quick-fix'' conversions, seemed capable of solution, at least partially. This was the direction in which to proceed: given a ship of large enough dimensions, a whole squadron of aircraft might be taken aboard.

As recounted earlier, the major impetus in carrier development during the First World War was provided by the need to address the menance of the *Zeppelin* airships. This called for fast-climbing aircraft to be embarked (preferably in reasonable numbers to offset serviceability problems and to create the best chance of successful interceptions) and a fast reaction time. The seaplane was hardly the ideal answer, its drag-inducing flotation gear ensuring a sluggish climb rate, although it could, it is true, be launched fairly rapidly from forward take-off platforms (given docile sea states) by means of trolley gear. On the other hand, wheeled aircraft could not be recovered by existing carriers, although they could ditch alongside and their pilots – if they were lucky – might survive. Alternatively, the latter might hope to make a convenient landfall nearby, if operating in coastal waters.

In fact, the safe recovery of wheeled aircraft was the greatest difficulty in the early years of carrier aviation: despite, for example, HMS *Furious*' size, her take-off deck was not of sufficient area to prevent

Above: The Imperial Japanese Navy was a strong proponent of the use of catapult-launched floatplanes, as seen aboard the IJN *Chiyoda*.

Below: With the landing negotiated successfully, a Kingfisher heads for the towed dolly. Once secured, it will be hoisted aboard ship.

Dunning from tipping off the side and losing his life, and her later landing-on deck aft, its forward crash barrier notwithstanding, was rarely used. The major problem was that posed by the currents and eddies set up by the superstructure amidships; incidentally, despite the provision of connecting gangways, moving aircraft forward from the landing-on-deck to the take-off deck was a time-consuming and tricky business.

The inevitable solution was a flush deck, unobstructed by any form of superstructure. However, apart from having to relocate the bridge and conning positions, this meant having to devise some alternative system for discharging funnel gases (at the same time, it was hoped, creating conditions in which smoke would not blow across the landing-on deck). Not for the first time in carrier history, a compromise was called for. In the design of HMS *Argus*, begun in 1916 as radical conversion of a cargo liner,

Right: The British carrier HMS *Argus* was based on the incomplete hull of the Italian liner *Conte Rosso*. Completed in August 1918 she could operate eighteen Sopwith Cuckoo torpedo-dropping aircraft.

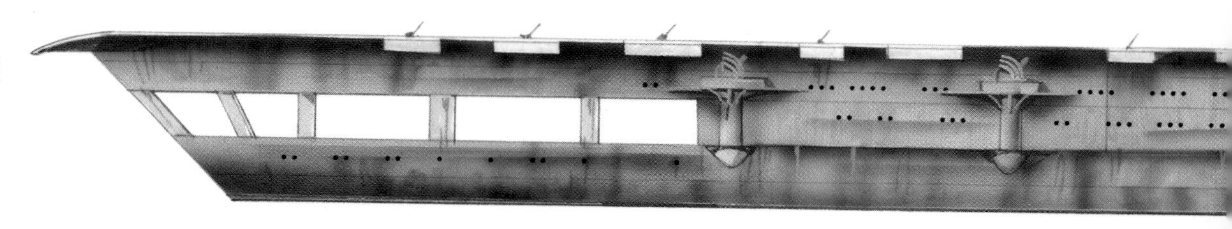

Right: A 1933 Japanese design-study in which the 1932 design (see page 35) had the flight deck extended to the bows, the guns removed, a massive stack in place of the downward venting funnel and, for the first time in a Japanese carrier, the stern plated over. But, as with the previous design, it was not built.

the boiler uptakes, instead of being led vertically in the conventional way, were led aft via trunking either side of the shelter deck, to discharge at the stern; the shelter deck formed the floor of a 330ft (100.60m) long hangar, which was topped by a three-quarter length flight deck. Lifts were installed to facilitate the movement of aircraft up from the hangar. At the preliminary design stage, a narrow, downward-sloping take-off platform extended over the forecastle, and an open quarterdeck, equipped with derricks, enabled aircraft to be handled over the stern: in truth, the ship was still effectively a seaplane carrier, not that far removed from existing vessels. However, it was anticipated that wheeled aircraft could be safely landed, a net barrier being slung between twin small superstructures either side amidships. In the event, HMS *Argus* was commissioned as a completely flush-decked carrier – the first in the world – devoid of any structure above her full-length flight deck.

Although HMS *Argus'* configuration was a major advance over that of the twin-decked HMS *Furious*, for example, and although the ship served for twenty-five years with little further alteration, it was not to be the final blueprint for all future carrier construction. HMS *Furious* was refitted for a third time after the First World War, to a broadly similar pattern, and a number of Japanese carriers were completed with fully flush flight decks: even as late as 1949, the US carrier USS *United States* was laid down as a flush-

Above: Bearing a passing resemblance to *Argus*, HMS *Audacity* was the first escort carrier to be completed in World War Two. Her six Martlet fighters were parked on the flight deck, since there was no hangar.

Left: The Japanese carrier *Akagi* was completed in 1927. Her two hangars each had a flying-off deck forward, although the middle deck was seldom used. The flight deck sloped upwards from the stern to a point just abaft the uptake and then downwards. Intended to help take-offs and landings, it proved unnecessary in practice.

Above: Having made a successful landing aboard HMS *Furious* in 1917, Squadron Commander Dunning tried a second. He came in high and stalled and the plane veered over the side.

decked ship. However, command, navigation, gunnery direction, air direction and communications all required clear sky arcs in order to function satisfactorily, and out of the jungle of conflicting views there emerged a general consensus that a single island structure, offset to starboard (the pilots' preference), would permit these tasks to be conducted effectively without compromising flight deck operations to an unacceptable degree. It is impossible now to say which of the ships under construction towards the end of the First World War was the first to feature a starboard island superstructure. HMS *Argus* was fitted with a dummy installation made of canvas in October 1918; HMS *Hermes* and HMS *Eagle* were both commissioned with permanent islands in July 1923 and February 1924 respectively; and the latter were preceded into service by the Japanese *Hosho*, which was commissioned at the end of 1922 with a simple island superstructure in place, although her design post-dated that of all three British carriers and was the beneficiary of considerable British assistance. Meanwhile, in the United States, the ex-collier USS *Langley* entered service in March 1922 as a flush-decked carrier with a hinged funnel outboard of the flight deck on the port side.

The flush-decked carrier with a small island to starboard has remained the

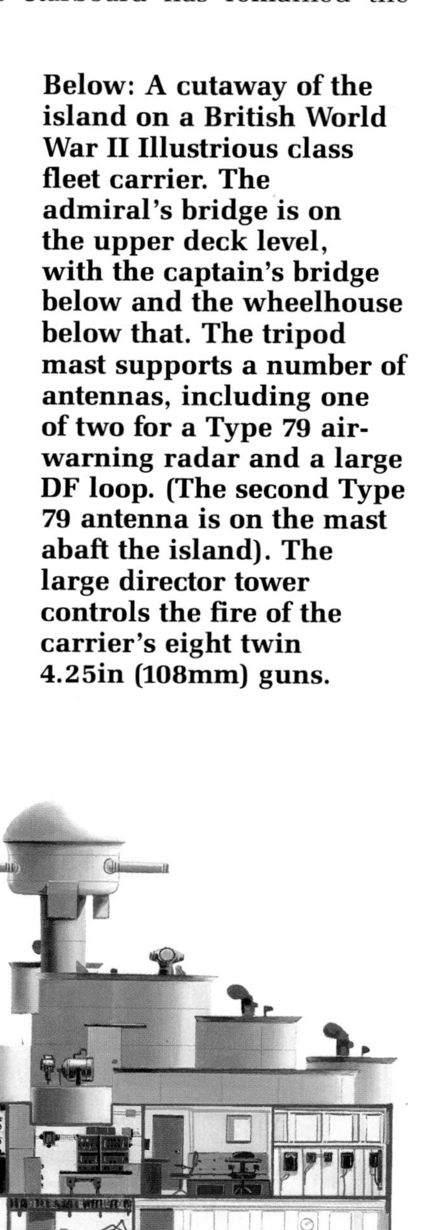

Below: A cutaway of the island on a British World War II Illustrious class fleet carrier. The admiral's bridge is on the upper deck level, with the captain's bridge below and the wheelhouse below that. The tripod mast supports a number of antennas, including one of two for a Type 79 air-warning radar and a large DF loop. (The second Type 79 antenna is on the mast abaft the island). The large director tower controls the fire of the carrier's eight twin 4.25in (108mm) guns.

standard pattern for the type. The geometry and character of the flight deck itself, however, have undergone considerable evolution, especially during the period from the end of the First World to the 1960s – and are still, to an extent, seeing changes today. Even as the full-length, stem-to-stern flight deck was gaining acceptance, the actual process of landing an aircraft aboard was being intensively studied, with a view to making it easier, faster and, above all, safer. Primarily, the effort went towards ensuring that an aircraft would be kept on a straight course while landing-on, and that it could be brought to a halt within a relatively short distance. Today, these requirements are met by means of transverse arresting wires – akin, in a sense, to the sandbag-weighed wires utilised by Ely for his famous exploit on board the cruiser USS *Pennsylvania* – aided by all manner of high-lift, high-drag, self-braking devices built into the carrier aircraft itself. With the slow landing speeds prevalent in the early-1920s, the problem was not so much that an aircraft could not be halted – a biplane travelling at 70kt and attempting to land on board a carrier steaming at 25kt into a 25kt headwind was flying at only 20kt in relation to the flight deck conditions – as that wind buffeting could make it veer off course. To cope, a system of longitudinal wires was installed on deck; hooks attached to an aircraft's axles would engage the hooks, keeping the machine on course as it rolled forwards. At the deck edge, palisades acted as windbreaks. However, damage to aircraft and sheer inconvenience (HMS *Argus*, for example, was fitted with over 50 wires during trials of the system) caused these wires eventually to be removed and the system abandoned altogether as a landing aid. The US Navy elected to install athwartships wires on its flight decks during the 1930s, while the Royal Navy abandoned any form of arresting mechanism for the time being, although retractable net palisades were

Below: A US Navy carrier task group in the 1950s. Ranged on the flight-deck of the Essex class carrier, USS *Philippine Sea* (CV-47), are (from front to rear) F9F-2 Panthers, F3D2 Skynights and AD-1 Skyraiders.

Above: The crowded flightdeck of a Casablanca class escort carrier (CVE), with nine Douglas SBD Dauntless dive-bombers and five Grumman F4F Wildcats visible; total air wing was twenty-seven aircraft. Fifty of these carriers were built between 1942 and 1944; all served with the US Navy.

Right: A busy scene on the flightdeck of USS *Enterprise* (CV-6) on 15 October 1944 as crewmen prepare aircraft for another operational mission in the Pacific campaign. Forward are four Grumman F6F Hellcats, one of the best carrier fighters of World War II, with Curtiss SB2C Helldiver dive-bombers behind and three more F6Fs right aft.

Right: A Grumman F9F Panther lands aboard USS *Oriskany* (CV-34) in the early 1950s. This pilot's view of a landing aboard a straight-decked carrier, shows the arrester wires, the "batman" and the crash barrier.

an insurance against aircraft careering over the side of the ship.

These seemingly minor differences in flight deck characteristics were in fact symptomatic of a deeper difference in philosophy between the two navies. British practice required the whole of the carrier flight deck to be used for take-offs and landings. Aircraft would be raised from the hangar by means of the after lift for take-off; on landing, aircraft would roll towards the forward lift, to be immediately struck down. In contrast, US carriers would land their aircraft, which would then be merely rolled to the bow; with landing operations completed, the aircraft would then be moved back aft (respotted) to the take-off position. Thus the flight deck came to be used not only for landing and take-off, but also as a kind of deck park. The apparent vulnerability associated with leaving aircraft topside would be countered by employing fighters to defend the ship; the Royal Navy preferred to remove carrier aircraft from the source of danger by taking them below to the hangar (which, in the wartime Illustrious class, was armoured), relying on fixed gun batteries and passive defence to defeat the threat. On a US carrier, a flight of landing aircraft would always see others parked ahead of it, at the bow (except perhaps the first machine to land), and it was therefore imperative to halt aircraft by means of arresting gear.

This was the major problem that would be solved by the introduction of the angled deck, which is designed into a modern fleet carrier as a matter of course. The invention was forced by the much higher landing speeds of jet aircraft, but,

Right: In contrast to the picture above, this cockpit view from a Grumman A-6 Intruder shows the clear path created by the angled deck, with the parked aircraft well out of the way.

Left: The flightdeck of the assault ship USS *Inchon* (LPH-12), reminiscent of World War II design, is intended only for helicopters and VTOL aircraft.

Above: The plane director on the flightdeck of USS *Saratoga* (CV-60) guides a Grumman A-6E onto the catapult ready for launch.

Above: USS *Kitty Hawk* (CV-63), with the flight deck crew preparing to launch a Vought A-7E Corsair II. The C13 steam catapult will accelerate the aircraft to flying speed in a distance of just 295ft (90m).

conveniently, the angled deck also permitted simultaneous launch and recovery – which had hitherto been hazardous if not impossible. There are other side benefits. For example, the more quickly the landing area can be cleared, the faster a flight of aircraft can come aboard; the faster it is recovered, the less time is spent by each individual aircraft waiting its turn to land, the less fuel is wasted and the greater the *effective* range at which a target can be hit – a particular concern if a mass strike of thirty or more aircraft is being organised.

It follows that the siting of lifts is critical; so is their number. A minimum of three lifts is generally accepted as desirable today, bringing up aircraft for take-off (now, since the introduction of the steam catapult for launches, sited forward instead of aft) and striking below those not required on the flight deck; the third lift (or the fourth in the case of a carrier with four) is a useful insurance in case of battle damage. Lifts are positioned away from the take-off and landing areas for obvious reasons; they are also undesirable amid the deck park and that is a feature of the dead area of the remainder of the deck. Hence deck-edge lifts are in general use. These have, of course, the advantage of minimising any weakening effect on the structural integrity of the flight deck and have been a common feature of US carriers since 1940. However, lifts must also be placed at locations convenient to the hangar below: they form part of the hangar "floor" as much a part of the flight deck. This goes some way to explain why early carriers had one lift situated a short distance from the bows and another a short distance from the stern, more or less along the centreline. As well as being convenient for flight deck operations, they were sited at each end of the hangar to leave a clear workspace.

Other flight deck aids represent safety equipment or are aimed at ensuring brisk flight-deck cycles consistent with safety. For example, sophisticated electronic landing aids are now available. Catapults, too, are indispensable: even given favourable wind conditions and any number of lift-inducing devices attached to the aircraft, it is not possible for a fast jet carrying a reasonable payload to take off conventionally in 800 to 900ft (244 to 275m), even if such a length of strip were available. The US Navy, which since pre-war days has been a strong advocate of the mass air strike, has for long courted the advantages of fast flight deck cycles and rapid response, and was therefore an early convert to the use of catapults. Moreover, the compelling advantage of the catapult, at least in its early days of service, was that it did not require the parent carrier to turn away into the wind in order to get its

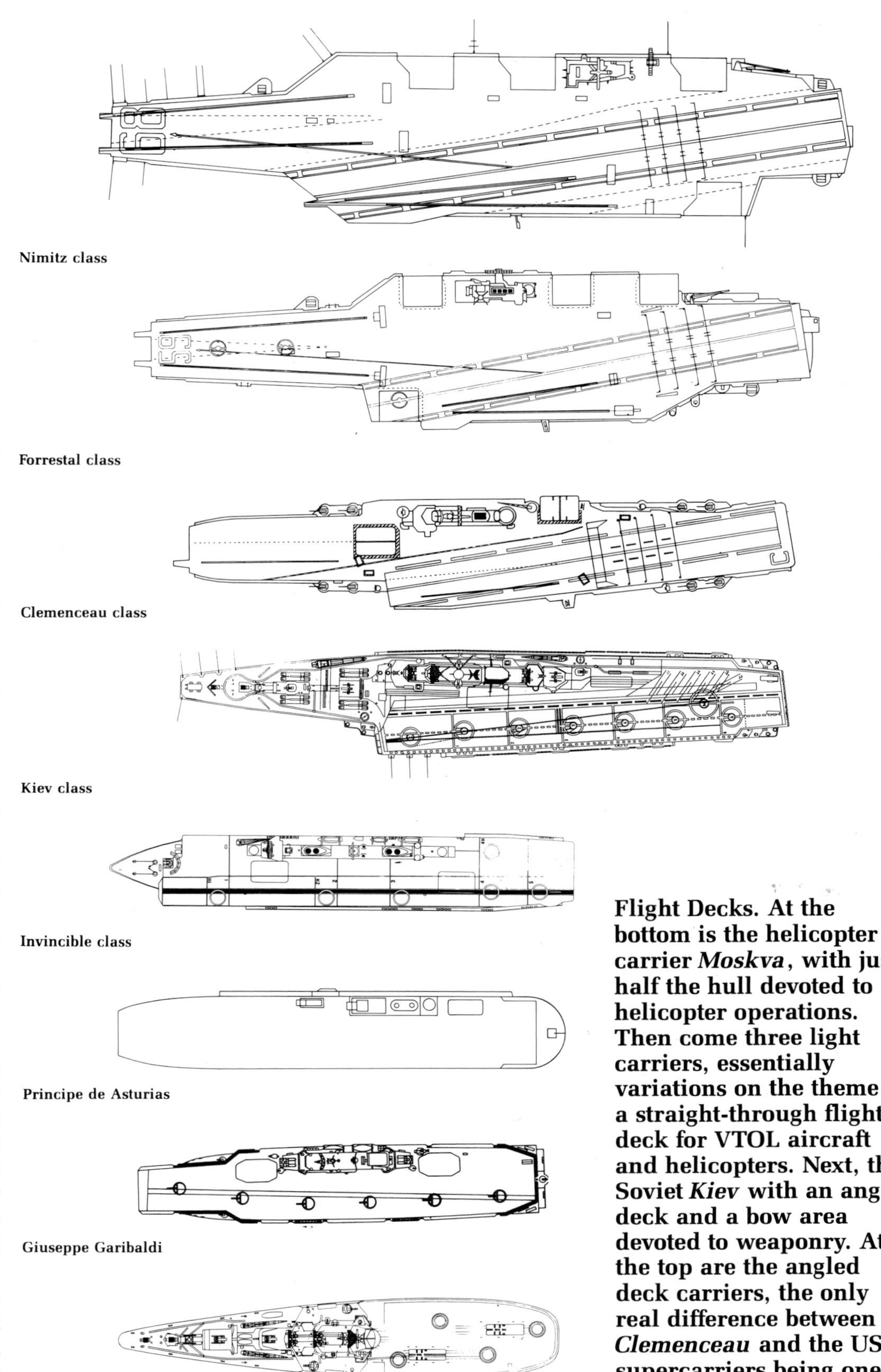

Flight Decks. At the bottom is the helicopter carrier *Moskva*, with just half the hull devoted to helicopter operations. Then come three light carriers, essentially variations on the theme of a straight-through flight-deck for VTOL aircraft and helicopters. Next, the Soviet *Kiev* with an angled deck and a bow area devoted to weaponry. At the top are the angled deck carriers, the only real difference between *Clemenceau* and the US supercarriers being one of sheer size.

Left: The ski-jump is one of the major advances in carrier technology, greatly enhancing the payload carried by a STOL aircraft, its only disadvantage being that it reduces the parking space on the flight-deck.

Right: A British Sea Harrier takes-off from a ski jump, a device conceived by a British officer, Lieutenant-Commander Doug Taylor, RN. One of its many advantages is that it requires no modifications to the aircraft.

aircraft off. Nowadays, also, the effects of jet exhaust more or less forbid conventional rolling take-offs, even if they were possible: only one or at most two jet aircraft could be spotted for take-off at a time.

There are other ways in which the carrier designer can assist laden aircraft to get airborne in short distances, although in general they impose severe operating penalties. The best known device is the Royal Navy's "ski jump", designed to increase the payload that can be carried by Sea Harriers (which can lift much more when performing a short rolling take-off than when rising vertically). The Harrier is a small aircraft, somewhat limited in capability when compared individually with, for example, US Navy front-line combat aircraft but, provided a small air group is acceptable, it does not require a very large flight deck from which to operate nor, therefore a very large and expensive ship. In fact, to some extent the "ski jump" can substitute for the catapult: it appears that the new Soviet fleet carriers have both systems. Indeed, it is perfectly possible to shorten take-offs by practically any type of aircraft by driving it up a ramp: more lift is generated for a given speed because the relative wing incidence is increased and the take-off roll is therefore shorter.

The carrier has, over the eighty years of its existence, evolved as an extremely effective naval weapons system; it has also, by and large, managed to respond effectively to the changing technologies imposed on aircraft. The two World Wars posed the greatest challenges to carrier designers, and these periods have coincided with (and provided the impetus for) the two great revolutions in carrier design: First World War experience established the basic layout of the modern carrier, bringing together diverse theories of the early war years to form a set of design "rules" that gained universal acceptance; and the Second World War spawned the jet aircraft, which forced a series of radical modifications to standard practices. For the present, despite the influences of V/STOL aircraft, a third revolution is not yet in sight.

Left: Compared to a full run from a level deck (top) the ski-jump enables an aircraft to either reduce its take-off run with the same payload (centre) or to carry a much higher payload for the same take-off run (below).

50
100
COLES

3

Strength in Depth

SINCE all of the nations that currently conduct air operations from aircraft carriers generally utilise a variety of fixed-wing aircraft and helicopters drawn from different squadrons, it is usual for a distinct command element to exist so as to co-ordinate the activities of these disparate components within the overall fleet structure. Thus, whether they be relatively lightweight vessels, such as Great Britain's Invincible class and France's *Clemenceau*, or massive nuclear-powered American super-carriers like the USS *Nimitz*, air operations will be directed by a unique organization which works closely with its surface warfare counter-parts to ensure that mission requirements are satisfied, and the naval battle group around the aircraft carrier function as a cohesive entity.

Below: Flight deck operations are extremely complex and there is much concurrent activity in a relatively small space, all of which requires close coordination. Here two catapult crew work beneath a Grumman A-6E as two plane directors stand-by, while a SAR helicopter takes-off behind.

Right: The military might of a US navy strike force is well shown in this picture. The carrier has some 85 aircraft embarked, which can undertake missions deep into hostile territory. This was demonstrated during the Gulf war by such groups operating in the Red Sea.

Left: HMS *Invincible*, together with HMS *Hermes*, provided the air support without which the British task force could not have retaken the Falkland Islands in 1982. The Invincible class normally carry one squadron of Sea Harrier fighters, one squadron of Sea King ASW helicopters and a flight of three Sea Kings converted to the AEW role.

In the case of Great Britain, which no longer operates aircraft carriers of the traditional type (i.e. with catapult and arrester gear), the Fleet Air Arm (FAA) came very close to leaving the fixed-wing flying business altogether and was fortunate in being able to turn to Vertical Short Take-Off and Landing (V/STOL) to form the fighter element of its contemporary carrier air groups. Nevertheless, these group organizations are small and seldom control more than about 15 aircraft and helicopters in peace-time, although their wartime complement would be boosted to around the 20 mark. Foremost amongst the equipment that is operated when deployed is the BAe Sea Harrier of Falklands fame. When deployed at sea, this potent V/STOL fighter equips a single squadron (normally with eight aircraft but rising to 12 in times of tension or war) which is tasked with satisfying air defence needs by establishing a fighter screen some distance from the parent carrier.

In much the same way, sub-surface threats are countered by a squadron with a handful of Westland Sea King

helicopters. Able to range out some way from the carrier, the Sea King HAS.5/6 contingent extends the defensive perimeter established by destroyers and frigates which, incidentally, also carry helicopters in the shape of the smaller Westland Lynx. Finally, there is an airborne early warning (AEW) component equipped with the Sea King AEW.2A, a pair of these helicopters normally being assigned on a detachment basis although a third would be added in the event of hostilities.

Fitted with Searchwater radar adapted from the BAe Nimrod maritime patrol aircraft, this AEW specialist evolved in the wake of the painful lessons learnt during the battle for the Falklands in 1982. Then, it was realized that new sea-skimming weapons such as the AM.39 Exocet could strike at the very heart of a battle group, even though they were launched from great range. In consequence, detection of aerial threats had to be achieved at the earliest possible moment if the threat posed by Exocet and other similar weapons was to be countered successfully. The result, in typical British style, was a hurried conversion of the Sea King, but despite the fact that it was a hastily contrived solution, it works well in practice and is now an integral part of air elements carried by HMS *Invincible* and its sister ships, HMS *Illustrious* and HMS *Ark Royal*. Again, the helicopter at some distance from the parent ship, employs its on-board sensor to probe the ether for threats and also expand radar coverage out beyond the horizon.

Left: A weatherbeaten HMS *Hermes*, the second of the Falklands carriers, returns triumphantly to Portsmouth at the end of the conflict. The last of the British traditional carriers, she has since been sold to India.

Above: A busy scene aboard a British Invincible class carrier. As can be seen, small carriers such as this often need to put their elevators within the flying area of the main deck, unlike the much larger US vessels.

Left: Though not quite as old as the surviving F-8E(N) Crusaders, the French Navy's Super Etendard strike aircraft can hardly be described as youthful. Plans in hand will see this warrior retired from service in the mid-1990s.

Air components embarked aboard aircraft carriers of other nations naturally vary, depending upon the ship and the equipment that is available. France, for example, still adheres to the conventional type of carrier, with the *Clemenceau* and *Foch* normally being able to accommodate an air group within the region of 30 aircraft and helicopters. Fixed-wing hardware carried at sea is composed of modest quantities of the Vought F-8E(FN)

Right: Small but very versatile, the Alouette III can perform a variety of carrier-borne duties, including light ASW and SAR. Clearly visible in this shot is one of the emergency flotation bags, located at the top of the main wheel strut assembly.

Crusader (for air defence), the Dassault-Braguet Super Etendard (for strike/attack), the Dassault-Breguet Etendard IVP (for reconnaissance) and the BreguetAlize (for ASW), while rotary-wing equipment consists of the Aerospatiale Super Frelon (for ASW) and the Aerospatiale Alouette III (for liaison and as 'planeguard during fixed-wing flying operations).

India, on the other hand, has remodelled its sea-going air power along British lines even though both of its carriers (INS *Vikrant* and INS *Viraat*) were originally of conventional format, with catapults and arrester gear. With the fairly recent retirement of the 'fifties-vintage Hawker Sea Hawk and the relegation of the ASW-dedicated Alize to shore-based tasks, the opportunity has been taken to install a ski-jump on the *Vikrant* (*Viraat* already had one, a legacy from its service with the Royal Navy as HMS *Hermes*) and it is the Sea Harrier which constitutes the cutting edge of Indian naval air power. These fighters are ably supported by variants of the Westland-produced Sea King and India is also known to be interested in adding an AEW capability, with the Sea King/Searchwater package evidently being Indias most favoured candidate at the present time.

Left: The largest helicopter now in service with the French Navy, the triple-engined Super Frelon is principally tasked with ASW duties. Carrier-borne operations are primarily conducted from the helicopter carrier *Jeanne d'Arc*.

Right: The Alouette III is also used by the Indian Navy aboard its carriers. However, their most important asset is the BAe Sea Harrier FRS.51. Both types are seen here on the flight deck of INS *Vikrant*.

While Britain has continued to pursue an innovative path in the field of shipborne air power by developing and deploying the V/STOL Sea Harrier, it has fallen to the USA to take the conventional aircraft carrier to perhaps its ultimate expression, and this nation continues to invest heavily in carrier borne aviation as both a means of protecting its interests overseas and of projecting its military might on a global scale.

When it comes to operating aircraft at sea, there can be little doubt that the US Navy (USN) leads the field in terms of both experience and capability. There are three main reasons for that. Firstly, it has more aircraft carriers than anybody else. Secondly, those carriers are rather bigger than anybody else's and are therefore able to accommodate more aircraft. Thirdly (and this is really no more than a function of the first two), it has more aircraft and aircrew than any other nation.

As far as exercising command over aircraft and helicopters embarked aboard a specific USN aircraft carrier is concerned, this is entrusted to organizations known as Carrier Air Wings (CVW), and it seems advisable to devote some time to considering the USN's awesome carrier force since its size and shape has exerted considerable influence on the size and shape of the CVW that can be embarked on each of these vessels.

Probably the single most important factor in moulding the contemporary CVW was the deployment of the so-called super-carriers. The battleships of the modern era, these massive warships have a total displacement around the 80,000 – 90,000-ton (81,280-91,450 tonnes) mark when fully laden, and they began to replace smaller vessels of the celebrated Essex class during the mid-1950s, at a time when Cold War confrontation between the superpowers loosened the purse strings and made vast sums of money available to the American military machine. One of the most tangible manifestations of that period of almost untrammelled spending on defence was the commissioning of the USS *Forrestal* on 1 October 1955, and by the end of the decade it had been joined by three sister ships in the shapes of the USS *Saratoga*, USS *Ranger* and USS *Independence*.

Four more similar vessels of the Kitty Hawk class followed from the slipways during the early to mid-1960s, while sandwiched between them was the USS *Enterprise*, a one-off which broke new ground by virtue of being the first aircraft carrier (and one of the first surface warships) to rely on the power of the atom as a means of propulsion when it entered service in the early-1960s. Most recently, from the mid-1970s on, the USN has deployed further nuclear-powered carriers in the shape of the Nimitz class, easily the biggest and certainly amongst the most powerful warships to be found anywhere in the world. Five of the latter are presently in service, and construction continues towards the objective of completing a further three before the end of the present century, even though each of them is a hugely expensive

Below: The US Navy has more experience than any other in large-scale operations from aircraft carriers. This view shows an F-14 Tomcat on quick-reaction alert status, with another moving up behind. The US Navy is totally committed to the massive investment needed to sustain carrier air power.

undertaking in terms of manufacturing effort and financial investment.

As far as distribution is concerned, the carrier force is split fairly evenly between the USN's two major Fleet organizations, namely the Atlantic Fleet and the Pacific Fleet. While inter-Fleet transfers do take place, these are generally fairly rare events, occurring mainly to remedy imbalances such as might arise when older vessels are decommissioned or when carriers are returned to the shipyards for major overhaul. Such a process is under way at present and there have been a number of changes recently, with more in prospect due to the imminent retirement of the elderly pair, the veteran USS *Lexington* and the USS *Midway*.

Right: USS *Forrestal* (CV-59) passes through the Suez Canal in August 1988 with 42 aircraft of various types on her flight deck. Her crew are making it obvious to any passing aircraft that they have been at sea for no less than 108 consecutive days, a demonstration of the carrier as a power-projection tool.

Left: The flight deck of USS *Saratoga* (CV-60) operating off the Libyan coast. A tractor pulls a Grumman A-6E Intruder forward to the catapult, with two F-14A Tomcats, two Vought A-7E Corsair IIs and a Lockheed S-3A Viking waiting their turn behind.

Below Right: USS *Eisenhower* (CVN-69) heads North through the Suez Canal in September 1990. The Gulf crisis had already begun and the canal would become vital for the deployment of Coalition naval forces.

Below: The Forrestal class carrier USS *Ranger* (CV-61) at anchor off Hong Kong in December 1987. *Ranger* is the only one of her class not scheduled to receive a Service Life Extension Program (SLEP) refit.

In service, with one notable exception, USN carriers are home-ported at major naval bases within the USA and are assigned to either the Atlantic Fleet's 2nd Fleet or the Pacific Fleet's 3rd Fleet. These numbered fleet organizations are tasked with controlling naval and aviation activities in the Atlantic Ocean and the Eastern Pacific respectively, but periods of sea duty in these areas are normally of relatively short duration, seldom exceeding three months at a time and most commonly undertaken for special tactical and operational exercises such as those that are frequently called by the multinational NATO alliance.

In addition, though, there are two other major areas of naval activity, specifically the Western Pacific and the Mediterranean Sea, and it is these areas which are the most usual destinations for extended periods of sea duty. During such intervals, carriers and other warships are detached from their normal fleet parent and reassigned to the control of a command agency that resides permanently in the area in question. Operational deployments to these regions generally last around six months, throughout which the carrier will form the centrepiece of a specialist battle force or Task Force under the direct command of a different numbered fleet agency. By way of illustration, in the Western Pacific, carriers (and other vessels in the Battle Group) will constitute Task Force 70, which is just one of a number of such forces under the command of the 7th Fleet, and also the organization which directs the activities of the sole carrier that is homeported outside the USA. Until recently, the USS *Midway* had this distinction, operating from Yokosuka, Japan, on a permanent forward deployed basis between 1973 and early 1991, but it has recently turned over its Oriental dockyard berth to the USS *Independence*, pending decommissioning in the USA and a one-way trip to the breaker's yard. Serious consideration was at one time given to utilizing a similar concept and forward-basing a carrier in the Mediterranean Sea, but this failed to come about. As a result, 6th Fleet carrier strike components assigned to Task Force 60, which serves as the battle force in the Mediterranean Sea, are deployed in their entirety from 2nd Fleet assets homeported on the USA's eastern seaboard. Mention has already been made of the CVW organization, and this is without doubt one of the most important departments in the complex organizational structure that exists aboard a carrier at sea. Each CVW

Above: During operations off Libya in February 1986 the commander of Task Force 60, Rear-Admiral David E. Jeremiah, USN, discusses the battle situation with a junior staff officer in the task force command-and-control center aboard USS *Saratoga* (CV-60).

Right: Commander Guy Myslivy, USN, the 'air boss' aboard USS *Saratoga* (CV-60) during a Red Sea deployment. He is engaged in overseeing the complex operations on the flight deck from the Primary Flight Control Station (''PriFly'').

Below: Orders start from the admiral and are given to the 'air boss'; eventually they reach the level where action is taken. Here orders are issued at a squadron briefing in VF-31's ready room aboard USS *Forrestal* (CV-59) in January 1990.

is headed by an officer who is universally known as CAG, this being a hangover from the 1950s when aviation elements at sea were concentrated into Carrier Air Groups (CAG) rather than CVWs. Responsible to the Captain of the carrier to which his CVW is assigned, the CAG is invariably the most senior combat leader in the CVW and will typically be of Commander rank, with around 20 years of service behind him as either a pilot or naval flight officer. He will also be vastly experienced, and that bank of experience is instrumental in allowing him to properly lead and manage the 2,000 or so officers

Above: Two Grumman C-2A Greyhounds wait for the catapults to be cleared so that they can depart USS *Forrestal* (CV-59). These COD (Carrier On-board Delivery) aircraft perform an invaluable role, carrying up to 32 passengers, 12 stretcher cases or 8,210lb (3,724kg) of cargo over ranges of up to 1,500nm.

and men assigned to the squadrons that come under his command, whether it be in battle or in more mundane peacetime tasks such as training. Not surprisingly, the position of CAG is a much sought after billet, for it is also an important rung on the ladder to the very top of the USN hierarchy and often presages a tour of duty as a carrier captain, American public law stipulating that aircraft carriers may only be commanded by rated naval aviators. However, since only 13 front-line CVWs exist at this present moment, the USN is in the happy position of being able to select only the best of the best to fill the few slots that are available.

As to the elements that constitute the CVW, the USN is now entering a period of change as it heads towards the 21st Century. A number of factors have influenced this decision, not least of which is the imminent demise of the last of the smaller Midway class carriers. That leaves the way clear for the service to move towards a standardised CVW organisation, something it has long desired and something that is at last seen to be within its grasp.

Throughout the 1960s and on up until about the mid-1970s, USN doctrine with regard to carrier operations was based upon the use of separate and distinct elements to perform attack and ASW missions, and there were two basic types of

Above: An early 1960s USN carrier task group with USS *Wasp* (CVS-18), five destroyer escorts, a fleet oiler and a diesel-electric submarine. Overhead fly nine S-3 Trackers, three AD-3 Skyraiders and four HSS-2 Sea Kings. This view makes an interesting comparison with that on page 48.

carrier in commission, namely the CVA (for attack) and the CVS (for ASW). At that time, the CVAs invariably deployed with an attack-orientated CVW, and these typically featured two fighter squadrons, two light attack squadrons and one medium attack squadron. To that hard core was added other elements – sometimes in the form of squadrons but often merely detachments – to satisfy specialist tasks such as AEW, aerial refuelling, reconnaissance and EW. Throughout this period, attack CAGs were embarked aboard the USN's newest supercarriers as well as the trio of Midway class vessels, but two of the older and much smaller

Above: A pair of McDonnell F-4B Phantom IIs of squadron VF-11, their hooks lowered, prepare to land. Originally designed for missile-armed fleet defence, the F-4 was developed into probably the greatest multi-role sea- and land-based fighter of modern times.

Right: Two stalwarts of the US Navy in the 1960s and 1970s aboard USS *Enterprise* (CVN-65). An F-4 Phantom thunders past a Douglas A-4 Skyhawk of squadron VA-93. The tiny A-4 was designed as a lightweight attack aircraft and contrasts with the two-seat, twin-engined Phantom.

Essex class carriers also supported force structures of this kind until as recently as the mid-1970s.

CVSs, on the other hand, went to sea with dedicated ASW CAGs, operating Grumman S-2 Trackers and Sikorsky SH-3 Sea Kings for the primary mission of sub-hunting, as well as a detachment of Grumman E-1B Tracers to provide a measure of AEW cover. In addition, it was by no means uncommon for these specialist CAGs to feature a limited air defence capability in the form of a few McDonnell Douglas A-4 Skyhawks, although it is doubtful if they could have done much to forestall a determined attacker. With effect from the beginning of the 1960s, aircraft carriers engaged in this valuable role were drawn entirely from the versatile Essex class and about 20 of these vessels eventually fulfilled this mission at various times and in various areas over an interval of some two decades.

By the dawn of the 1970s, however, it was becoming apparent that the days of these long-serving warships were numbered, especially since the replacement for the Tracker would be the turbofan-powered Lockheed S-3 Viking, a type that offered a massive increase in qualitative capability while at the same

Above: The Grumman E-1B Tracer was a modification of the S-2 Tracker and was fitted with a huge teardrop-shaped radome containing an early warning radar antenna array. This enabled the task group to have much greater warning of the approach of hostile ships, aircraft and missiles.

Left: Aboard an ASW carrier in the 1970s, its flight deck covered with Grumman S-2 Trackers and two E-1B Tracers. The rear of each of the S-2 engine nacelles housed eight disposable sonobuoys.

time allowing significant quantitative reduction. In essence, the advent of the Viking was a classic illustration of the adage less is more, for far fewer Vikings could perform far more effectively. Once that fact was absorbed it was a logical step to try and accommodate them aboard the large deck supercarriers.

So was born the multi-purpose CV, this being the last major change to be made to CVW structure. Under this philosophy, the CVSs were paid-off, the specialist CAGs were disestablished, and the Tracker and Sea King squadrons that were made surplus by this move were reassigned to certain CVWs on a permanent basis. Eventually, of course, the S-3A Viking began to assume responsibility for the ASW mission and the long-serving Tracker was steadily retired. Implementation of the CV concept was undertaken during the mid-1970s, and basically entailed the addition of a 10-aircraft S-2 or S-3 squadron and an eight-aircraft Sikorsky SH-3 Sea King squadron to CVWs on the larger carriers. Later, as the number of Sea Kings in the USN inventory declined, the complement of each SH-3 squadron was cut to six when at sea.

By the close of the 1980s, CVW structure had evolved further and four distinct types of organisation were in use, with complements that varied from a low of 66 to a high of 86 aircraft. Three of these types were found only aboard the supercarriers, while the fourth was confined to the two remaining Midway class vessels (USS *Midway* and USS *Coral Sea*), which, by virtue of being smaller, were unable to accommodate quite so many aircraft

Left: A Lockheed S-3 Viking ASW aircraft, the type which took over from the S-2 Tracker in the mid-1970s. The two General Electric TF-34 turbofans give an unrefuelled range of some 2,300miles (3,700km).

Above: A McDonnell-Douglas F/A-18 Hornet climbs away from USS *Coral Sea* (CV-43). Developed from a Northrop lightweight fighter concept, the Hornet excels in attack, reconnaissance and fighter roles.

and helicopters.

Looking first at the USS *Midway* and USS *Coral Sea*, these featured a CVW organisation named after the latter vessel, which was first to deploy with a somewhat revised complement. Fighter and light attack missions were entrusted to three squadrons with the McDonnell Douglas F/A-18 Hornet, each being equipped with 12 aircraft when at sea. Medium attack potential rested with the Grumman A-6E Intruder, some 16 examples normally being embarked, and these invariably included a few that were fitted with buddy refuelling pods. ECM and AEW tasks fell to Grumman EA-6B Prowler and Grumman E-2C Hawkeye squadrons, each with a total of four aircraft, while half-a-dozen SH-3 Sea Kings were available for ASW and planeguard duties.

As it transpired, the USS *Coral Sea* was withdrawn from service at the end of April 1990, and the sole survivor of this three-ship class – the USS *Midway* – was itself earmarked for retirement during the course of 1991. In both instances, however, the CVWs previously assigned (CVW-13 and CVW-5 respectively) are to remain in existence although the CVWs will be increased in size and reorganized slightly so as to permit their operation from larger carriers of the Forrestal, Kitty Hawk and Nimitz classes.

Below: Grumman EA-6B Prowlers in "air-show" formation. This aircraft is the standard airborne EW platform for the US Navy, with surveillance receivers mounted in the tail pod and active jammers in underwing pods.

Above: Aboard USS *Saratoga* (CV-60) Tomcat and Corsair crews await their turn on the catapult. The F-14s' wings are in the 'oversweep' position intended to reduce space requirements on the flight deck and in the hangar.

Below: With most of her aircraft on deck, USS *Kennedy* (CV-67) shows the composition of an early 1980s USN Carrier Air Wing. Air defence, strike, recce, EW, AEW, ASW and transport assets are all shown.

Gradual evolution resulted in the creation of what is now known as the Conventional type of CVW, with a typical large-deck aircraft carrier usually deploying with a complement of 86 aircraft and helicopters. Fighter forces remained constant at two squadrons, each with 12 aircraft. The McDonnell Douglas F-4 Phantom II was used for much of this period, but this once dominant machine has now been retired from the inventory, leaving the Grumman F-14 Tomcat as the USN's premier fighter. Regardless of which fighter type was flown from a particular carrier, sister squadrons invariably used the same type, but it should also be noted that one Tomcat squadron usually includes a trio of Tactical Air Reconnaissance Pod System (TARPS)-configured machines in its complement.

The light attack contingent is also composed of two squadrons. In this instance, the veteran Vought A-7 Corsair II is now in terminal decline, having been almost entirely ousted by the rather more potent and certainly much more versatile F/A-18 Hornet during the past decade. Typical

Above: The 1960s A-7 Corsair light strike aircraft set new levels of accuracy when first introduced, and modifications such as the infra-red sensor pods seen here kept it an effective weapon.

complement is 12 aircraft per squadron and, once again, sister squadrons always operate the same type. Turning to the medium attack component, this has relied solely on the somewhat unattractive but supremely effective A-6 Intruder since the last of the piston-powered Douglas A-1 Skyraiders were withdrawn from the front-line in the late-1960s. In a Conventional CVW, only one squadron is present and this normally operates 10 attack-dedicated A-6Es alongside a quartet of KA-6D tankers.

As already noted, the S-3A Viking and SH-3H Sea King are responsible for ASW tasks, squadron strength being 10 and six respectively, leaving the balance of the CVW to be made up of four EA-6B Prowlers for ECM and four E-2C Hawkeyes for AEW. It is this conventional CVW that is most widely used at present, with 11 of the 13 active CVWs already organised along these lines or due to be so in the very near future.

The two exceptions are also worthy of closer scrutiny, especially since one of them sign-posts future developments in this important field. This is CVW-8, which currently operates from the USS *Roosevelt*, while the other – CVW-2 on the USS *Ranger* – is a hangover from the experiments of the early-to mid-1980s, when the USN was exploring other CVW configurations. Foremost amongst those was the Kennedy CVW, which first appeared when CVW-3 embarked aboard the USS *John F. Kennedy* in the early-1980s. In that experiment, attack-dedicated elements were greatly altered, with both A-7 Corsair II light attack squadrons remaining ashore. Instead, the *John F. Kennedy* went to sea with a pair of Intruder squadrons, each of which operated a dozen A-6E aircraft, while one also had four KA-6Ds. Other than that, the mix remained unchanged, giving an overall complement of 76 aircraft and helicopters, and it is perhaps worth mentioning that

CARRIER AIR WING COMPOSITION

Aircraft	Coral Sea	Kennedy	Roosevelt	Conventional	Transitional
F-14A/A+/D	—	24	20	24	20
F/A-18A/C	36	—	20	24	20
A-6E	16	24	20	10	16
KA-6D	—	4	—	4	—
EA-6B	4	4	5	4	5
E-2C	4	4	5	4	5
S-3A/B	—	10	10	10	8
SH-3H/SH-60F	6	6	6	6	6
Total	66	76	86	86	80

Above: USS *Ranger* (CV-61) was one of the two carriers used to develop the new ''Roosevelt CVW'', although she herself will not be able to operate the F/A-18 until 1993. Meanwhile she is the last operating a ''Kennedy wing''.

Below: The carrier USS *Kennedy* (CV-67). Below the overflying Tomcats are two F-14s on one deck-edge lift, with an S-3 Viking beside them using a small area of deck to maximum advantage!

CVW-3 was unofficially referred to as the Grumman CVW due to the preponderance of hardware originating from this famous manufacturer's New York factories. Eventually, this CVW reverted to the more familiar conventional format, but CVW-2 on the USS *Ranger* continues to employ the Kennedy formation and is not expected to switch to a conventional CVW format until Fiscal Year 1993, when the USS *Ranger* will have been modified to permit operation of the McDonnell Douglas F/A-18 Hornet.

Pioneering work done aboard the USS *John F. Kennedy* and the USS *Ranger* laid the basis for the Roosevelt CVW which made its debut in 1988 – 89. As its title implies, this first appeared aboard the USS *Roosevelt*, when CVW-8 embarked with ten squadrons operating a grand total of 86 aircraft. Interceptor elements consisted of two F-14 Tomcat squadrons (each with 10 aircraft) while dedicated attack forces comprised two A-6E Intruder squadrons,

each again having 10 aircraft. In this instance, however, no specialist KA-6Ds were present, aerial tanker requirements being accomplished by standard Intruders fitted with the buddy refuelling stores noted earlier. Also on board were two 10-aircraft F/A-18 Hornet squadrons, this so-called swing-fighter being sufficiently versatile to operate with little or no loss of effectiveness in either interceptor or attack roles. Thus, CVW resources can be quickly adjusted to meet wide and varied threats.

Other forces embarked on the USS *Roosevelt* were made up of single squadrons engaged in a variety of tasks, with each of the four squadrons involved operating a different and unique type. Five E-2C Hawkeyes satisfied AEW requirements, and an identical quantity of EA-6B Prowlers was available for ECM work. Finally, ASW needs were met by 10 S-3 Vikings and also by half-a-dozen SH-3 Sea Kings.

It is this CVW configuration that will ultimately be adopted as standard across the Fleet, although implementation has had to be deferred for a number of years and the reorganization is not expected to be completed until the early part of the next century. In the meantime, the USN is to adopt a broadly similar variation that will be known as the Transitional CVW: this will have an identical number of squadrons but will possess only 80 aircraft, with four A-6E Intruders and two S-3 Vikings being omitted.

Perceived as a kind of stepping stone on the path to adopting the Roosevelt CVW structure, the decision to switch to the transitional CVW was taken by the Chief of Naval Operations during November 1988. With the solitary exception of the Roosevelt CVW which is to continue to operate in that form, it will be implemented on a Fleet-wide basis during the early part of the present decade.

ACTIVE CARRIERS BY FLEET

Atlantic Fleet

Name/Pennant Number	Carrier Air Wing	Remarks
USS Forrestal (CV-59)	CVW-6	To be reassigned to training duties as AVT-59 in summer in 1991.
USS Saratoga (CV-60)	CVW-17	
USS America (CV-66)	CVM-1	
USS John F. Kennedy (CV-67)	CVW-3	
USS Dwight D. Eisenhower (CVN-69)	CVW-7	
USS Theodore Roosevelt (CVN-71)	CVW-8	
USS George Washington (CVN-73)	—	Due to commission in December 1991, probably with CVW-6.

Pacific Fleet

Name/Pennant Number	Carrier Air Wing	Remarks
USS Midway (CV-41)	CVW-5	Homeported at Yokosuka, Japan but due to retire in 1991.
USS Ranger (CV-61)	CVW-2	
USS Independence (CV-62)	CVW-14	Due to be homeported at Yokosuka, Japan during 1991.
USS Kitty Hawk (CV-63)	—	To complete Service Life Extension Program overhaul in 1991.
USS Constellation (CV-64)	—	Due for Service Life Extension Program overhaul 1991-93.
USS Enterprise (CVN-65)	—	Undergoing recore of nuclear reactor.
USS Nimitz (CVN-68)	CVN-9	
USS Car Vinson (CVN-70)	CVW-15	
USS Abraham Lincoln (CVN-72)	CVW-11	

Notes: As will be apparent, there is a marked imbalance with regard to distribution of carrier forces between the two major fleets, with the Atlantic Fleet possessing seven (soon to fall to six) while the Pacific Fleet has nine (soon to fall to eight). The equation is further complicated by the fact that the Atlantic Fleet has seven active CVWs while the Pacific Fleet has only six. However, changes are under way and these should result in the imbalances being redressed although it is not yet clear as to precisely how this will be achieved. At one time, it was expected that the USS Kitty Hawk (CV-63) would join the Atlantic Fleet but this plan has been changed and it now seems feasible that either the USS Constellation (CV-64) or the USS Enterprise (CVN-65) will transfer on completion of shipyard work that is presently in progress. This would then give the Atlantic Fleet a total of seven carriers (i.e. one for each of the seven CVWs). Alternatively, one of the Atlantic Fleet CVWs could be reassigned to the Pacific Fleet, an action which would also largely overcome the apparent anomaly in force distribution. In either instance, the 'spare' carrier could well be used to provide 'cover' for the overhaul of other vessels.

Right: Short-range ASW is normally carried out by helicopter, and the most recent addition to the US Navy is the Sikorsky SH-60B Sea Hawk LAMPS-III. This one from HSL-43 prepares to take-off from the deck of USS *Constellation*.

4

The Floating City

IN the vague half-light that heralds the imminent sunrise, the vast and imposing bulk of the aircraft carrier is only faintly visible from the escorting frigate which maintains a respectable distance to starboard as it steams along the flat, calm sea at a steady 15 knots. Up on the frigate's bridge, the small number of officers and ratings who are on duty are looking forward to the end of their shift, but remain constantly alert to the risk of collision; a risk heightened by the fact that thick patches of sea mist are occasionally encountered, reducing visibility to almost nil in a matter of seconds and necessitating reliance on radar to ensure safe separation from other vessels as the complex formation of the Carrier Battle Group sails on.

Hidden from view on the far side of the carrier, a supply ship steers a parallel course just a few yards away, a profusion of cables and lines physically connecting the two vessels during this potentially hazardous operation. They have been joined together in this fashion for more than an hour with thousands upon thousands of gallons of oil and aviation fuel having been pumped aboard to restock the carrier's own storage tanks in anticipation of an intense period of flight operations.

Below: An essential and never-ending task as USNS *Navasota* (T-AO 106), a Mispillion class replenishment oiler, refuels USS *Saratoga* (CV-60). *Navasota* is a unit of the large fleet of auxiliaries operated by Military Sealift Command (MSC), which gives global support to the US Navy.

Right: In the cold light of an Indian Ocean dawn a technician aboard USS *Kitty Hawk* (CV-63) checks the cockpit of a Grumman F-14 Tomcat. A large group of technicians are needed to keep such complex aircraft flying in the harsh operational environment of the world's oceans.

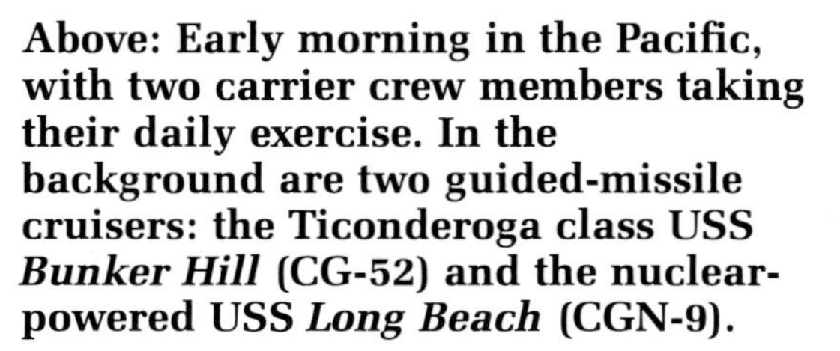

Above: Early morning in the Pacific, with two carrier crew members taking their daily exercise. In the background are two guided-missile cruisers: the Ticonderoga class USS *Bunker Hill* (CG-52) and the nuclear-powered USS *Long Beach* (CGN-9).

Below: On the bridge of USS *Kitty Hawk* (CV-63) a quartermaster plots the ship's course. Despite the plethora of electronic sensors and computers aboard a modern super-carrier, there is still a place for old-fashioned chart-work and manual instruments.

Aboard the carrier, some early risers brave the chill of early morning to observe the resupply activity from catwalks and deck edge elevators, while others, for whom this spectacle has long since palled, take the opportunity to grab some exercise by jogging from one end of the four-and-a-half acre flight deck to the other and back again, taking care to avoid tripping over the four arrester wires that lie in wait for the unwary towards the stern of the vessel. Elsewhere, maintenance personnel work on some of the 50 or so aircraft that are parked in seemingly haphazard fashion. Still others tend the so-called "yellow gear", which includes towing tractors and start carts. Apart from the occasional expletive prompted by a stubborn bolt or slippery spanner, the scene is one of orderly calm. As yet, there is little indication of the dangerous and frenetic activity that will crowd the deck in a matter of hours.

Deep inside the carrier, yet more men are hard at work and have been so since long before the first inklings of dawn. Air Wing operations staff spent most of the

Left: Lieutenant Scott Gunell, USN, quietly reviews his preflight notes in one of the squadron ready rooms aboard USS *Saratoga* (CV-60). The aircraft are the best that their country can buy, packed with the very latest technology, but they are flown by men such as this, upon whom the success of each mission totally depends.

previous evening drawing up the day's air plan, receiving inputs from all of the embarked squadrons and building them into a smooth and ordered programme which should allow all these parties to achieve their day's objectives. The programme has since been issued to the various interested departments and is now being studied by a number of bleary-eyed pilots as they down the first of a succession of mugs of coffee while they prepare for the day's first launch. Part of that process of preparation entails a series of detailed pre-flight briefings, which are now under way in several of the squadron ready rooms dotted about in odd corners below the main decks.

In the engine spaces which occupy the bowels of the ship, engines tend the boilers that provide the vital steam for the turbines which propel the 90,000 ton (91,440 tonnes) warship as well as the quartet of mighty catapults without which the carrier would be unable to project air power across the vast tracts of the world's oceans. For many of these men, their daily routine is almost entirely a subterranean one and it is by no means unknown for some of them to go for weeks on end without seeing daylight or breathing air that is untainted by the smell of oil. Their's is a hot and noisy working environment, as well as a highly uncomfortable one;

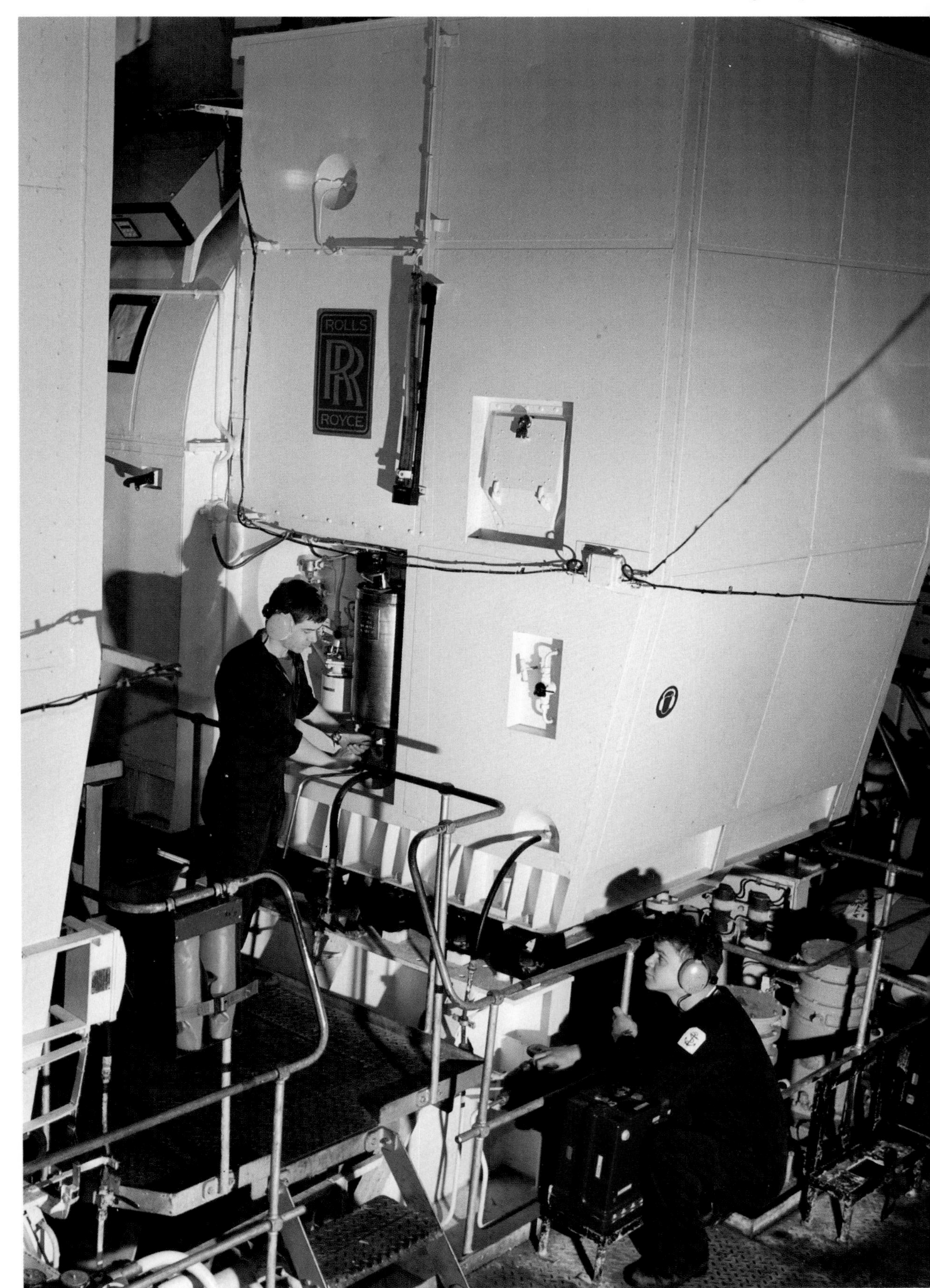

Right: Far below the flight deck two British artificers carry out maintenance work on one of their carrier's four Rolls-Royce Olympus TM3B gas-turbines. Both wear ear-protectors to prevent hearing damage from the high-frequency engine noise, but the engine-room environment is far cleaner and healthier than it would have been in the days of steam.

but these are amongst the most important individuals aboard, for without them the carrier would soon be reduced to nothing more than an impotent, vulnerable hulk, unable to take evasive action should it come under threat.

The various galleys that are scattered around in the ship's spaces are doing good business, this morning as personnel drift in to partake of breakfast. Some eat heartily, piling their plates high with fried food; others are more conservative in their eating habits, confining themselves to just a couple of slices of toast, either out of respect for dietary considerations (it is all too easy to overeat and gain weight aboard ship) or, more commonly, for the simple reason that they cannot face ''real'' cooked food so early in the day.

Right: Sailors on board USS *Independence* (CV-62) take a meal break. On a carrier with a crew of some 5-6,000 men, about 20,000 meals will be served daily, requiring 1,500 loaves of bread and no less than 1,300 gallons (4,920 litres) of coffee!

Left: 19th March 1986 and Mess Specialist Third Class Billy West is oblivious to the air operations off the Libyan coast in which his ship, USS *Coral Sea* (CV43), is involved. He knows that his professional reputation is placed on the line three times a day on every day of every cruise.

For the various elements which have responsibility for the catering, the task more demanding than that faced by Jesus when called upon to feed the 5,000, and breakfast aboard ship is nothing more than just another mealtime to be got through. The sheer magnitude of the catering requirement can perhaps best be understood by quoting a few statistics. During a typical 24-hour period the hard-pressed cooks will prepare close to 20,000 meals; feeding the ship's complement of 6,000 seems never-ending. For every week that the ship is at sea, almost 10,000 loaves of bread will need to be baked and some 6,000 gallons (27,276 litres) of fresh milk will be consumed. Even more extra-

ordinary is the fact that close to 10,000 gallons (45,460 litres) of coffee will be swallowed in every seven-day period – one could perhaps be excused for reaching the conclusion that this beverage is almost as important as oil in allowing the huge warship to function efficiently as a weapon of war.

On the flight deck high above, a number of tugs are cranked up as handling crews set about the job of "re-spotting" aircraft and clearing the bow and waist catapult track areas as a prelude to the day's first launch. Some warplanes are sent below to the hangar deck for routine maintenance while others – which have been restored to flight status – are raised to take their places. Within half-an-hour or so, order is restored and four aircraft that are due to fly first are positioned ready for launch, with nose-tow links hooked up to the catapult shuttles and hold-back bars securely in place.

Above: Maintenance work goes on night and day, with these men fixing faults on a somewhat dented Vought A-7E Corsair II aboard USS *Saratoga* (CV-60). Despite the Red Sea's scorching heat the hangar is cool.

Below: The maintenance work done, a Grumman F-14A Tomcat is raised on one of the USS *Kennedy*'s (CV-67) elevators to the flight deck, to be fuelled, armed and handed over to the pilot for another mission.

Left: USS *Forrestal* (CV-59) with three Grumman F-14A Tomcats waiting to take off. AE-110 (on the catapult) and AE-105 both belong to Fighter Squadron VF-11, while AE-203, with its nose hard up against the jet-deflector is from Fighter Squadron VF-31. The squadron coats-of-arms are prominently displayed on the fins.

On the port bow catapult, an F-14 Tomcat carries a clutch of AIM-7 Sparrow and AIM-9 Sidewinder air-to-air missiles, this being one of two such fighters that are kept on alert, ready to be fired off at a moment's notice in the event of an unanticipated threat being detected. Adjacent to it, an E-2C Hawkeye is hooked up and unless there is a sudden scramble this will be first to be catapulted skywards, moving out to set up its orbit some way from the carrier to provide extended radar coverage for

the other air elements. Once on station, it will begin monitoring air traffic, relaying information it gleans electronically to the parent ship and to airborne interceptors by means of sophisticated secure data link equipment.

Further down the bow, a Sea King helicopter is the subject of some activity, as deck crew spread its rotors while others perform a pre-flight inspection and gather up the vivid red ''Remove Before Flight'' streamers from various points on the airframe. Soon, it too will be powered up, ready to clatter off noisily and take up a position abeam of the carrier where it can quickly be called upon to perform the plane-guard rescue function if its services are needed. On board will be a parajumper and a winchman, both highly qualified specialists in the discipline of retrieving aircrew from the sea, and their timely intervention can, on occasion, make all the difference between life and death to a downed pilot.

Moving aft, one of the waist catapults is occupied by the second alert Tomcat which stands next to a KA-6D Intruder, it being usual for one of these tankers to launch early so as to be ready to provide in-flight refuelling support in the event of an emergency. Other warplanes stand in tight clusters, ready to follow the first four into the air in quick succession once flight operations begin.

Directly ahead of the island superstructure rests a gaggle of A-6E Intruders. All have their wings folded, but the symmetry and uniformity of the line is broken by the longer shape of an EA-6B Prowler. Suspended from hardpoints beneath its wings and belly are five slab-sided objects which, to the untutored eye, could well be taken for some unusual form of bomb or air-delivered weapon. That is far from

Left: Another scene on the flight deck of the USS *Forrestal* (CV-59) as the plane director signals to the captain of a Grumman E-2C Hawkeye AEW (Airborne Early Warning) aircraft. The E-2C is lined up on the catapult and the pilot is standing-by for the order from the plane director to spread the aircraft's wings immediately prior to take-off.

Above: The engines of the Sikorsky SH-3 helicopter are running and the pilot has just been given the signal from the plane director to start the rotors (''burning' and turning''') before take-off. Helicopters are used for ''plane-guard'' duties, ready to rescue crews from ditched aircraft.

Below: Just after lifting-off, this Sikorsky SH-3D of Helicopter Squadron HS-3 is about to undertake plane-guard duties. Among those in the cabin are a parajumper and a highly-trained winchman, both experts in the very rapid reactions required to save downed aircrew.

Left: Awaiting their turn for take-off are three Grumman A-6E Intruders and a single EA-6B Prowler. The very sophisticated EA-6B has a four-man crew and provides the strike force with the electronic warfare cover essential for modern air operations.

being true, however, for these objects actually contain transmitters which are used to generate high-powered jamming signals that can very quickly render an opponent electronically ''blind''. In so doing, they provide protection for friendly strike forces and no strike pilot in full possession of his faculties would relish the prospect of taking on a modern air defence network without support from the Prowler.

Just a few yards away, facing the Intruders and the Prowler, are a number of F/A-18 Hornets, both these and the A-6Es carrying weapons racks on which are suspended several of the diminutive blue

Below: A Grumman EA-6B Prowler has been towed forward to the catapult and awaits the final preparations prior to launch. Two flight deck men communicate with each other using hand signals, the only reliable method in the deafening noise and bustle of revving jets, roaring turboprops and clattering helicopter rotor blades.

Right: Immediately prior to launching from USS *Coral Sea* (CV-43) a crewman carries out a final visual check on the security of an underwing fuel tank on a McDonnell-Douglas F/A-18 Hornet. Great dependence is placed upon the intelligence, alertness and initiative of such men to prevent potential disaster.

Mk.76 25lb (11.35kg) practice bombs. Able to simulate the tactics and techniques employed in the delivery of full-size weapons, practice bombs are infinitely less expensive and many thousands of them are routinely expended by attack squadrons engaged in operational training. A shotgun-type cartridge in the nose of the Mk.76 provides visual evidence of the impact by a flash and puff of smoke, and allows range personnel to score each and every delivery.

Further aft, behind the island and around the fantail, are more aircraft which will go on the first ''push''. Most are F-14 Tomcat interceptors, blackened gun ports

Right: Despite the use of mechanical aids the arming of carrier aircraft still requires a lot of men and involves a great deal of pure, old-fashioned muscle power. These live bombs are being attached to the underwing hardpoints, a very manpower-intensive task, as is clear from the picture.

Above: Two aviation ordnance men trundle a trolley carrying three Mk 20 Rockeye-II cluster bombs across the flight-deck of the USS *Coral Sea* (CV-43). The bombs will be loaded onto the underwing stations of a McDonnell-Douglas F/A-18 Hornet.

on several providing visible confirmation that a number of fighter pilots have recently completed air-to-air gunnery practice, firing against a towed banner target. Again, they also carry practice weapons in the shape of inert Sparrow and Sidewinder missiles with seeker heads that can be activated during simulated air combat training routines. In this way, pilot and radar intercept officer pairings can practice and polish proficiency with either radar-homing or heat-seeking weapons without the risk of actually shooting down an adversary and so

Left: Amid all the hustle, bustle and clamour on the flight deck of the USS *Kennedy* (CV-67), a maintenance crewman uses great care and patience to impart a final polish to the windscreen of a Grumman F-14A Tomcat, just before the pilot comes to make ready for the day's operations.

Above Right: On the flight deck of USS *Eisenhower* (CVN-69), a Lockheed S-3A Viking of Air Antisubmarine Squadron VS-31, stands secured to the deck with wings folded. Note the unusual asymmetric wing-folding arrangement, designed to reduce the overall height.

scoring an expensive ''own goal''.

Bulkier shapes are visible around the stern. These are S-3 Vikings, with a vital role to play in protecting the battle group by performing anti-submarine warfare operations and, should it prove necessary, by attacking sub-surface threats with depth charges or homing torpedoes. Beneath a Viking, technicians are busy inserting sonobuoys into ejection chutes located in the plane's belly, this being just one of the sensors that may be employed in the sub-hunting role.

Right: These sonobuoys are dropped from ASW aircraft at heights of 100-40,000ft (330-12,200m) to descend under a drogue parachute. Their batteries are activated on contact with seawater and at the end of a preset operating life they sink themselves automatically.

Above: On the flight deck of USS *Saratoga* (CV-60) two members of the flight deck crew confer with the aircrew of a Grumman F-14A Tomcat during the course of their pre-flight inspection of the aircraft. These meticulous checks ensure the safety of aircrew, deckcrew and equipment.

Left: 'One for the family album!' as the proud pilot of a Grumman A-6E Intruder aboard USS *Kitty Hawk* (CV-63) poses for the cameraman.

Right: A member of the fuel crew makes a careful check of his papers during the start-up procedures on board USS *Saratoga* (CV-60). It is vital that fuel loads are correct, not only to enable the aircraft to fly its mission but also because the precise weight must be known for the catapult.

''Pilots, man your planes'' blares tinnily from loudspeakers in ready rooms and at strategic locations throughout the carrier, aircrew hastily swallowing a last mouthful of coffee before gathering up their helmets, life vests and sundry other accoutrements that they will take aloft. Most have already donned the impedimenta that is such an essential adjunct to flight in today's high-performance warplanes, but some hurry off to nearby locker rooms where they hastily don their G-suits, preferring to delay the moment of putting on this somewhat uncomfortable and confining garment until as late as possible.

From his viewpoint in ''Pri-Fly'' (Primary Flight Control), high above the deck in the island superstructure, the air boss lowers the microphone and glances out of the window, to see the first of a stream of aircrew emerge from an open hatchway below. In ones and twos, threes and fours, they come; their numbers depending upon the type of aircraft that they will fly. Some are purposeful in their intent, striding rapidly towards the machine that they are due to fly. Others are more leisurely, looking briefly skywards, perhaps as if to assess the accuracy or otherwise of the morning's met. briefing, or glancing off to port, where the grey shape of the oiler is still visible as it withdraws into the distance, its resupply function completed. Still others are more boisterous, cracking jokes and jostling

Above: Aboard USS *Saratoga* (CV-60) the ''air boss'' and operations officer look down from ''Pri-Fly'' during air operations against Libya in March 1986. The side of the bridge is adorned with heraldic artwork.

Above: In the Primary Flight Control station an officer and crewman use colour-coded models to maintain a precise plot of aircraft positions and movements on a schematic representation of the flight deck. Such detailed control is essential for the safe and efficient running of a crowded flight deck.

Above Right: Housework on the grand scale as one crewman steam-cleans the flight deck on board USS *Coral Sea* (CV-43) in the Mediterranean, while a second operates a massive vacuum cleaner! They are removing oil and grime from the yellow landing lines, which must be readily visible to returning pilots.

each other as they scuffle to pass through the hatch out on to the deck, where they disperse in different directions to their machines.

Regardless of demeanour, they are all business when they reach their aircraft, setting their helmets down or handing them to a member of the deck crew, before beginning a rapid pre-flight inspection. While it may be fast, the speed comes of experience and these seemingly cursory inspections are actually very thorough and complete.

At a Tomcat, a radar intercept officer clambers up the access steps and quickly but carefully settles into the aft cockpit, where he busies himself with some ''switchology''. Below, his ''driver'' checks the feline beast, reaching up and running his right hand quickly along the sleek Sidewinder missile on the port rail to check that it is securely mounted, before ducking underneath to examine the main undercarriage assemblies and then scuttling aft to look at the massive horizontal tail surfaces. His examination then takes him to the rear, a quick glance at the exhaust nozzles confirming that all is looking good. Moments later, with the check complete, he climbs the short distance to the cockpit and begins strapping-in, assisted by a crew member who verifies that certain ejection seat safety pins have been removed and stowed in their designated slots. Then, finally, the ground crew member hands the pilot his helmet from its perch on the canopy bow, before climbing back down the ladder to the flight deck.

Ahead of the island, there is a moment of concern as a Hornet pilot discovers a loose panel, but this is quickly sorted out by a maintenance chief who drives home the offending fasteners. The pilot peers closely at the panel, almost as if he expects it to fall off before his eyes. It doesn't, and after a few seconds inspection he shrugs and moves towards the cockpit and climbs up the ladder.

At the bow, a motley assortment of men are gathering in a line which extends across the breadth of the flight deck. Most are clad in overalls and all wear coloured jerseys, flotation vests and helmets, the colours providing an instant clue to the nature of their duties. Those in blue are aircraft handling crew and chock men, while a clutch in canary yellow are more senior handling officers and plane direc-

Right: In a space below the flight deck two sailors man the catapult console and check aircraft launch weight against steam temperature and pressure gauges. If the figures are within the prescribed limits one will press the ''first ready'' button to confirm to the flight deck that all is well for launching the aircraft.

tors. Many wear green but they could be responsible for arrester gear, catapults, maintenance or ground support equipment, the only clue as to their department being a symbol on front and back of the safety vests.

Regardless of responsibility, they are awaiting the order to start the ''FOD walkdown'', a pre-requisite to all flight operations in which they will walk the length of the carrier while carefully scanning the deck and removing any loose object or material that could be blown about or ingested by a jet engine or propeller wash and cause injury to personnel or damage to aircraft.

With the tedious but necessary ritual complete, the tannoy crackles into life again, background chatter in ''Pri-Fly'' being evident for a second or two before a disembodied voice issues the command to start engines, an action that coincides with the carrier turning to port so as to head into wind. Such is the bulk of the vessel, however, that this manoeuvre is hardly perceptible and it is only by looking at the curving wake and the shifting position of the recently-risen sun that one is able to confirm the change of course.

In little more than a matter of seconds, the muted whine of generators is swamped by a deeper roar as pilots in close to 20 aircraft at various positions on the huge flight deck run rapidly through their engine start procedures. Hidden from view, turbines begin to revolve under the pressure of compressed air, and fuel starts flowing into combustion chambers where it quickly ignites. For the deck crew, this is the right moment to don ear defenders, since the noise will soon reach such a pitch that normal voice communication becomes all but impossible.

At such times, training takes over, with the whole team operating almost on ''autopilot'' as they run through the launch procedure that has been well drilled into them during extensive pre-deployment work-up periods and long months at sea since the cruise started. To the inexperienced eye, the next few minutes appear wholly chaotic at best, and it is necessary for the uninitiated to

Below: The plane director uses hand signals to communicate with other members of the deck crew on board USS *Eisenhower* (CVN-69). Red-jacketed ordnance men wait behind him, ready to be called forward for a last-minute check of fuzing and arming pins. Weapons safety is vital on the crowded decks of a carrier.

Above: The plane captain uses a hand signal to direct the pilot of a Grumman E-2C Hawkeye to increase his port engine to full power. The aircraft belongs to Carrier Airborne Early Warning Squadron VAW-137, on board USS *Coral Sea*.

Above: More muscle-power as a flight deck crewman tugs an electrical cable across the deck of USS *Eisenhower* (CVN-69). He is hurrying to connect an aircraft to the ship's electrical supply to enable pre-start checks to take place.

Below: Crewmen stand-by with aircraft chocks aboard USS *Eisenhower* (CVN-69) whilst taking part in NATO Exercise West Wind in the North Atlantic in August 1988. They are dwarfed by the tail of a Grumman A-6E Intruder.

Below: As final preparations are made for the launch the Grumman F-14A Tomcat starts to sweep its wings forward from the 'over-sweep' position. Despite the huge size of a carrier the jolt from the release of the catapult is felt through the ship.

Right: A green-vested 'hook-up man' on the catapult crew watches carefully as a McDonnell-Douglas F/A-18 Hornet edges forward to connect to the catapult "shuttle". The thick "tow-bar' is permanently attached to the undercarriage leg.

watch several launches before it is possible to discern a pattern as catapult crews and others scurry about in continuous but evidently random and disconnected action.

On the four catapults, the aircraft that were pre-positioned are very quickly dispatched skywards, with jolts that can be felt throughout the ship as they are launched. Within moments, the large blast deflector plates behind each catapult track are lowered flush with the deck, clearing the path for successive aircraft to move into position. Guided by hand signals from a plane director, an F-14 taxies cautiously forward, its twin nosewheels passing on either side of the shuttle. As it moves, the nose-tow bar is lowered to engage a receptacle at the front of the shuttle, another hand signal instructing the pilot to brake. Just as the Tomcat stops, a green-vested hook-up man hurries forward to check that the big fighter is correctly positioned and that the restraining "hold-back" link is also securely connected.

Close by, another crewman holds aloft a board and waits for the pilot to glance his way and verify that the figure quoted on it corresponds with the launch weight out of the aircraft. Thumbs up – all is well and the figure is quickly dialled into the capacity safety valve system which will

ensure that sufficient steam pressure is built up to safely launch the fighter. Below decks, a repeater relays this figure to a console operator who checks steam temperature and pressure gauges. All is in order, so he in turn presses the "first ready" button, which notifies the catapult crew that the launch procedure can safely continue.

Above: Grumman F-14A Tomcat, AE-106 of Fighter Squadron VF-11, is lined up on the catapult, almost ready for launch from the carrier USS *Forrestal* (CV-59). Note how close the second F-14A – AE-100, the personal mount of Captain Richardson, the Commander Air Group (CAG) – is to the tail-pipes of this aircraft.

Below: While the catapult crew are shrouded in smoke from the catapults, more aircraft await their turn for launch from USS *America* (CV-66). The third of the Kitty Hawk class, *America* was launched in 1964 and commissioned in 1965. She has three 295ft (90m) C13 catapults and one of the 16ft (5m) longer C13-1 type.

211
OFFICER

215

Above Left: The catapult officer, crouching low, his left arm parallel to the deck, uses two extended fingers to show that all is ready for launch of an F-14 Tomcat. Within half-a-second he will drop his left hand to touch the deck and a crewman will press a button to ''fire'' the catapult.

Above: A Tomcat starts its climb away from the port catapult of the USS *Kennedy* (CV-67) as a Marine Corps Intruder prepares to follow. The four catapults on *Kennedy* enabled her to maintain a high launch rate, essential for launching large multi-squadron co-ordinated strikes.

By now, the hook-up man has hurried back to the narrow portion of deck between the catapults which provides a safe haven for launch crews during this operation; and most people's eyes are now firmly locked on the Catapult Officer, who signals to the deck edge firing station to hit the ''bridle tension'' button. The F-14 twitches slightly as the Catapult Officer instructs the pilot to release the brakes and then, with a circular hand signal, to move the throttles to full power.'

At the rear of the Tomcat, bright tongues of flame spear out from the twin engine exhaust nozzles as the afterburners kick in, superheated air being impelled against the blast deflector plate and diverted upwards in a yellowish tinged haze. The pilot scans his instruments for indications of a problem, finds nothing amiss and turns to look at the Catapult Officer, before sketching a nonchalant salute which indicates he is ready for launch. Looking around to check that all is indeed ready, the Catapult Officer crouches lower, with one arm extended horizontal to the deck. Half-a-second later, he drops his arm and touches the deck with his fingers, which instructs a crewman in the catwalk to depress the firing button.

Unable to withstand the sudden increase in pressure, the hold-back link disengages and the Tomcat begins its short but violent journey down the flight deck, to be almost literally flung into the air. Behind it, wraiths of steam pour from the catapult track, only to be quickly

Left: A Grumman F-14 Tomcat, its afterburners blazing, rockets along the deck with its mainwheels still just on the flight deck but its nosewheel already clear of the catapult. No matter how experienced the pilot, this is a tense moment that can never be ''just routine''.

Overleaf: The magnificent spectacle of a Grumman F-14A Tomcat of Fighter Squadron VF-2, afterburners roaring and flaps half extended on its fully swept-forward wings, climbing and banking away from a catapult launch. Within seconds its undercarriage and flaps will be retracted for the climb to transit altitude.

NE

NAVY

dispersed as the shuttle is returned in readiness for the next aircraft, which is even than rolling forward over the now lowered blast deflectors.

And so it continues, this scene being re-enacted at all four catapults until there are no more aircraft left to launch and

Left: The catapult officer on board USS *Coral Sea* (CV-43) signals that a Grumman A-6E Intruder is ready for launch. Another crewman sits nonchalantly in the haven area in the centre of the deck watching the action.

Below: The scene from the catwalk as the twin turboprops of a Grumman E-2C Hawkeye develop full power immediately prior to a catapult launch from USS *Saratoga* (CV-60) in the Mediterranean.

something approaching silence returns. Within minutes, though, fresh activity ensues, as tow tugs begin to manoeuvre another wave of aircraft into position for the day's second launch, which gets under way some 90 minutes later. Again, some 20 aircraft are rapidly despatched; but as the last one lurches into the air, F-14s from the first "push" are flying overhead from astern, their pilots "hawking the deck" to visually ensure that the launch has ended and that the angled deck landing area is clear for the recovery phase to begin.

Recovery procedures vary in accordance with prevailing weather and visibility. Today, ceiling and visibility OK (CAVOK) conditions prevail and a "Case 1" recovery ensues, this being an entirely visual procedure with no radio communication or use of landing aids such as the Automatic Carrier Landing System (ACLS) which depend on electromagnetic radiation. In this instance, aircraft "stack" in a race-track pattern above the carrier at clearly defined holding altitudes, only descending to a lower level as space becomes vacant.

Alternative landing modes are "Case 1" (1,000ft [305m] ceiling and five miles [8km] visibility) and "Case 3" (bad weather and/or night), with aircraft being directed by air traffic controllers on the carrier or in an E-2C Hawkeye. Under this procedure, the first to aircraft recover will begin its approach from an altitude of 5,000ft (1,525m) at a distance of 20 miles (32km) astern of the carrier. Number two to land will be at 6,000ft (1,1830m) and 21 miles, (33.80km), with number three starting at 7,000ft (2,135m) and 22 miles (35.40km) and so on.

Flying in sections of two to four, recovering aircraft continue to orbit and descend, making their final pass on the same heading as the carrier and slightly

Right: F-14A Tomcats, having completed their mission, are in the circuit over a carrier, while below them the deck is still crowded. An A-6E and an A-7E prepare for launch from the bow catapults, whilst the angled landing deck is occupied by several other F-14s.

Above: The landing signals officer (LSO) makes careful adjustments to his control console, which is integrated with the Fresnel lens optical landing system. This system of lights indicates to the pilot his position relative to the optimum glide-slope.

Below: The view from the co-pilot's seat in a Grumman E-2C Hawkeye as it makes its final approach for a landing on board USS *Ranger* (CV-61). From this viewpoint the angled deck looks far too short and narrow for such a large aircraft to land in!

to starboard (on the ''dead'' side of the vessel) at an altitude of about 800ft. On reaching a point some way ahead of the ship, each section initiates a break to port so as to introduce a degree of separation between individual aircraft – ideally, this will allow them to land at about 40-second intervals, which is just about the minimum time normally required for an aircraft to be brought to a halt, disengaged from the arrester wire and moved clear of the landing area.

By the time they are established at about 600ft (183m) pilots are mentally preparing themselves for landing as well as configuring the aircraft according to clearly defined checklists. Flaps, landing gear and the all-imporant arrester hook will be lowered; air brakes will be deployed to reduce speed, and inertia-reel seat harnesses will be locked so as to prevent injury from involuntarily hitting the instrument panel under the brisk deceleration that is a part and parcel of every successful ''trap''.

The base leg is initiated at sufficient distance to allow the aircraft to be established on final approach in a wings level attitude with about 15 seconds of flight to go before landing. Depending on

type, speed will be in the region of 120-150kts (138-172mph/222-272km/h) and the pilot will be looking for the "meat-ball", a device that provides him with visual clues as to whether he is flying the correct approach path or if he is arriving too high or too low.

More correctly known as the Fresnel Lens Optical Landing System, it is an amber light which appears at the centre of a mirror, itself actually a vertical row of five lenses. To fly a perfect approach, the pilot must keep the "meat-ball" aligned with a row of horizontal green lights adjacent to the central portion of the lens. Too high, and the illuminated portion will appear on one of the two upper lenses; too low, and it will be on one of the lower ones. So, if a pilot "flies the ball" correctly, he should engage the number three wire (of four) and earn himself an "OK Three" grading from the Landing Signals Officer (LSO), who monitors every approach and "trap" from a platform sited on the port side of the carrier flight deck.

Left: The LSO and his assistant stand poised, watching an incoming aircraft. The LSO can advise the pilot by radio or, in extrme cases, he can order an overshoot by pressing the button in his right hand which will activate flashing red signal lights.

Below: An F-14A Tomcat of Fighter Squadron VF-74 engages the second (of four) arrester wires on USS *Saratoga* (CV-60), scoring an "OK, Two." The approach was fractionally low, since ideally, the pilot should have engaged the third wire.

The LSO is himself an experienced aviator and a regular flyer who uses his expertise to grade every approach, and there is keen competition to win the "Top Hooker" trophy that is usually awarded to the most consistent pilot in the whole Carrier Air Wing on completion of a deployment. Even though it is the responsibility of the pilot to make the landing, the LSO can intervene – by either voice or light signals – if he is of the opinion that an approach is unsafe and that advice is necessary. In extreme cases, he can also order a "wave-off" by using a switch that he holds to illuminate two columns of flashing vertical red lights located adjacent to the "meatball". On seeing this signal, a pilot has no option but to comply by initiating an overshoot and re-entering the landing pattern for a fresh approach attempt.

Today's first recovery is going smoothly, with all bar one of the F-14s and F/A-18s landing at the first attempt. Now, it is the turn of the A-6s. On the opposite side of the deck, the Arrester Gear Officer adjusts the tension of the arrester wire engines to the typical landing weight of the Intruder then scans the deck to check if the area is clear. To his right the last Hornet to come aboard has still to move off to the bow parking area, so he delays depressing the dead-man's switch in his hand.

At the LSO's platform, an assistant watches the light that is controlled by the switch. It remains red, so he continues to intone the phrase "foul deck" every few seconds. Barely half-a-mile (0.80km) out, with flaps and undercarriage down, the first Intruder flies a curving path as it approaches its sea-going home, levelling out and continuing to bore on in for landing as the pilot visually acquires the "meatball".

"Foul deck . . ."

Right: The view from the LSO's platform as a McDonnell-Douglas F/A-18 Hornet, with flaps, undercarriage and arrester hook hanging down, comes in to land on USS *Coral Sea* (CV-43). The tension in the LSO and his assistant is clear as they monitor the aircraft on every foot of its final approach.

VMF

Left: A Lockheed S-3 Viking on its final approach, with wings level and a speed of approximately 130kts (150km/h). Throughout the landing process the pilot must be aware that if he makes an error, or if he is instructed by the LSO, he must immediately commence an overshoot, applying full power to enable him to regain altitude and try again.

Above: A Grumman A-6E Intruder just about to engage the wire, although its port main wheel has hit the deck marginally before the starboard wheel. Sparks are flying from the tip of the arrester hook as it scrapes along the deck, while inside the aircraft the crew are about to be slammed forward in their harnesses by the fearsome deceleration.

In the cockpit of the Intruder, the pilot fine-tunes the throttle settings to ensure that he maintains the correct glide slope and rate of descent as the grey shape of the carrier grows ever larger in the windscreen. Almost off-handedly, he makes a mental note that the deck is obstructed.

''Foul deck . . .''

Wingtip speedbrakes deflect up and down as the Intruder comes ever nearer, and the LSO is within seconds of illuminating the wave-off lights when the Arrester Gear Officer sees the final Hornet move beyond the foul line and instantly depresses his dead man's switch. Across the deck, the assistant sees the red light link out, to be replaced almost instantaneously by green.

''Clear deck . . .''

The LSO relaxes his grip on his switch and watches the Intruder, which seems to wobble slightly as it crosses the fantail, before settling rapidly with a jarring thud that disturbs those in the decks below who are trying – and, for the most part, failing – to grab some well-earned rest between duty. The noise and vibration of flight operations resounds through the ship.

Sparks fly from the tip of the arrester hook as it skitters along the surface in search of an arrester wire, the bomber's engine note rising as full power is applied to cover for an unsuccessful attempt at landing, or ''bolter'' as it is known amongst the select fraternity who earn their livelihood in this fashion. On this occasion, the hook finally engages a wire, causing the nosewheel oleo leg to compress and the heads of the pilot and bombardier/navigator to rock forward as their moving aircraft is brought to an abrupt halt close to the edge of the angled deck.

Power is smartly retarded and the Intruder is allowed to roll backwards for a few feet under the tension of the wire as a green-jacketed ''hook runner'' lurks in attendance to confirm that the arrester

Above: Having disengaged its hook, a freshly-recovered Grumman E-2C Hawkeye of Carrier Early Warning Squadron VAW-122, folds its wings as it taxies rapidly clear of the landing area, freeing it for the next aircraft.

Below: The day's flying over, the technicians return to continue their never-ending task of maintaining these complex aircraft. Here, a USS *Kitty Hawk* (CV-63) crewman works in the cockpit of an F-14 Tomcat.

cable has disengaged satisfactorily. Within moments, it is hauled back to be reset for the next arrival, which is already stabilized on final approach and fully configured for landing. As the cable moves, so too does the recently landed Intruder's nose wheel swivel, the pilot nudging the throttle levers in order to add just enough power to propel his aircraft clear of the landing area in accordance with hand signals given by a succession of yellow-suited plane directors who marshall it towards the bow where it will join other freshly-recovered aircraft. As it moves, the outer wing panels automatically hinge upwards and begin to fold, making it look for all the world as if the Intruder is flexing its muscles, like a bird, anxious to take flight again.

Behind it, another jarring impact announces the arrival of the second Intruder in a welter of sound and smoke – and so it goes on, until all elements of this 20-strong package of aircraft are safely aboard. The landing operation ends with

the arrival of a stranger, but a welcome one at that, for the newcomer is a Grumman C-2A Greyhound bringing urgent spares and supplies as well as mail for the ship's company.

Its arrival sends a buzz of anticipation through the carrier and it takes no more than a few minutes for word to reach most of the 6,000 or so crew who are now nearing the end of an arduous six-month deployment, interrupted by only a handful of brief periods of liberty at foreign ports. Letters from home are one way in which they can escape – even if only briefly – from the pressures, discomforts and dangers that are an ever-present facet of operating high-performance aircraft from ships at sea for periods that may last for up to six months at a time. But while some of the crew relax, catching up on news from home, others are beginning their shift; the whole crew working together to ensure that operations above and below deck continue smoothly and effectively around the clock.

Above: Sodium-oxide lamps illuminate the flight deck of USS *Eisenhower* (CVN-69) to enable work to continue into the night. Such lighting would obviously not normally be feasible in a combat environment.

Below: The sun sets over the Pacific as USS *Ranger* (CV61) steams northwards along the coast of California. Inside the ship several thousand men will be working, preparing the ship and its aircraft for tomorrow's operations.

5

Air Power

AT the present time, just eight of the world's nations are in the business of operating aircraft from ships at sea, with vessels in use ranging from relatively small carriers with a normal operating complement of about 20 aircraft, such as Argentina's *25 de Mayo*, right up to the real ''heavyweights'' of the United States Navy, which carry at least 80. In addition, a ninth country, Brazil, has only recently had to face up to the prospect of henceforth conducting maritime operations from shore bases, due to the fact that serious defects have been detected on its one and only carrier, the *Minas Gerais*.

Commissioned as long ago as 1960, after service with both the Royal Navy and the Royal Australian Navy as the *Vengeance* between 1945 and 1953, cost considerations apparently preclude rectification and it now looks certain that Brazil will have no option but to scrap this elderly warship, while plans to obtain a replacement now seem unlikely to reach fruition. Once again, it is the question of cost that is the principal stumbling block and this seems certain to prevent any new navy, save, perhaps, that of Japan, from acquiring warships for the projection of air power.

So, for the foreseeable future, it looks as though the carrier ''club'' will be confined to just eight members, namely Argentina, France, India, Italy, the Soviet Union, Spain, the United Kingdom and the United States of America. Between them, they operate a total of about 30 carriers, and this chapter will examine the capabilities of the aircraft and helicopters that are to be found aboard those carriers and the missions that they are sometimes called upon to fulfil.

Until quite recently, such a survey would have been a much easier task, in so far as fixed-wing aircraft and helicopters each tended to function in fairly clearly defined areas, with the only real overlap being encountered in the anti-submarine warfare (ASW) role. Today, however, such lines of distinction have become increasingly blurred. Part of that results from the deployment of genuine multi-mission aircraft and part from the advent of new weapons. Thus, by way of illustration, the McDonnell Douglas F/A-18 Hornet is able to perform both air defence and strike/attack missions, while suitably-modified Westland Sea King helicopters are now employed in airborne early warning (AEW) and can also undertake maritime attack by virtue of being compatible with sea-skimming guided missiles like the AM-39 Exocet and the British Sea Eagle.

Missions performed by aircraft and helicopters operating from aircraft carriers fall into five clearly definable categories: air-to-air, air-to-surface, ASW, electronic warfare (EW) and AEW. However, as will be seen, most of these categories embrace a rather broader spectrum than might at first be apparent.

Right: 14 tons of F-14A Tomcat thunder off the end of the angled deck, having been accelerated over a very short distance to flying speed by two afterburning TF-30 jet engines, augmented by the steam catapult. Operating high-performance aircraft such as this at sea requires a level of skill and daring beyond anything required of land-based aircrew.

100

Left: Sitting in the F-14 Tomcat's front ''office'', the pilot keeps his eyes on the deck marshall in front, responding to a series of well-rehearsed hand-signals that will guide him to a pre-determined slot on the deck. There he will wait until his aircraft is called forward for the elaborate drill that necessarily accompanies a carrier deck launch.

Taking air-to-air operations as a starting point, these are presently performed by just four basic types of aircraft. Most numerous and certainly most capable is the mighty Grumman F-14 Tomcat, which is currently flown by some 22 deployable US Navy (USN) fighter squadrons (VF), plus four Reserve units and two training outfits. Eventually, the number of combat-ready deployable squadrons is expected to rise to 26, allowing two full units to be assigned to each one of the 13 Carrier Air Wings (CVWs) that are currently in US Navy service.

Production of the Tomcat is continuing at a fairly slow rate, with new-build aircraft from the Grumman line now being to F-14D standard. A long-overdue improvement on the basic design, this addresses the often embarrassing problems that have been experienced with the Pratt & Whitney TF30 turbofan engines. Efforts to ''fix'' the TF30 alleviated, but did not entirely eliminate the shortcomings, and it was not until the advent of the F-14A+ in the late-1980s that the USN began to take delivery of aircraft with the more powerful, more economical and more reliable General Electric F110 engine. This has the virtue of allowing ''carefree'' handling throughout the flight envelope, pilots in the past having had to exercise caution when flying TF30-powered machines. No such restraints apply to the F110 and pilots are thus able to operate more confidently and, perhaps of rather greater importance, more aggressively.

The F-14A+ was, however, merely a stepping stone in the process of updating the Tomcat, and the F-14D also features digital avionics and a Hughes AN/APG-71 radar amongst other improvements. Between them, these changes should result in the Tomcat remaining a viable and potent adversary until well into the 21st Century, and the US Navy presently anticipates receiving approximately 400 examples of the F-14D. Unfortunately for Grumman, only 37 of those are expected to be new-build machines, since production is scheduled to terminate in 1993. As a result, other F-14Ds will be obtained by a Conversion in Lieu of Procurement (CILOP) programme, under which around 350 existing F-14A and F-14A+ aircraft will be updated to the latest configuration.

Missions undertaken by the Tomcat vary from providing defence for the various assets which constitute the Task Force (ForCAP: Force Combat Air Patrol) through barrier air defence against retaliatory air attack (BarCAP: Barrier Combat Air Patrol) to target cover for attack elements operating in hostile airspace which might themselves come under threat from enemy fighters (TarCAP: Target Combat Air Patrol).

Needless to say, weapons carried by the USN's premier fleet fighter vary according to mission requirements, but the Tomcat's killing potential has been and

Above: Despite the cold and driving rain there is a mission to be flown. Advancing at a snail's pace the mighty F-14 Tomcat is manoeuvred into position and then locked into the shuttle of the steam catapult.

Left: After elaborate and careful checks by a host of participants everything is ready. The final signal is given and the aircraft is shot forward by the catapult to complete another successful launch.

remains unique for it is still the only warplane that is able to operate with the Hughes AIM-54 Phoenix, a missile that is still unmatched in the air-to-air combat arena, even though it was first deployed more than 15 years ago. Subsequent improvement of Phoenix has allowed it to keep pace with developments in other fields, and it seems set to form an important part of the Tomcat's arsenal for many years.

Even though it has never been used in anger, perhaps the most outstanding aspect of the Phoenix is its remarkably long ''reach'', with development and other test-related trials clearly demonstrating that it possesses the ability to engage and destroy multiple targets at ranges of the order of 80 miles (128 km). That kind of capability is ideally suited to the so-called BarCAP fleet defence mission, this being the outermost element of a ''layered'' defensive doctrine.

In this, pairs of F-14s establish a protective ''screen'' at a considerable distance from the parent carrier. While that may at first seem to have the drawback of requiring lengthy transit sectors to be flown to the CAP orbit, extended times on station are made possible through the use of inflight refuelling, allowing fighters to remain airborne throughout a ''double-cycle'' period (i.e. for about 3½ hours). Working in close co-operation with the Grumman E-2C Hawkeye AEW platform, they form the first line of defence against threats from the air, and in that context the Phoenix missile is quite obviously a valuable tool in that it is able to destroy an enemy long before he begins to pose

Above: A night launch and a time-sequence exposure give a beautiful illustration of an F-14 Tomcat's take-off, showing the dip as it leaves the flight deck and then the smooth climb as it pulls away into the sky on another mission.

Left: Many millions of dollars worth of aircraft jammed together on the flight deck of USS *Enterprise* (CVN-65). But, the skilled professionalism of the flight deck crew and those in 'PriFly' will sort them all out.

a threat to the continued well-being of fleet elements. Maximum Phoenix load is six missiles per aircraft (as well as a brace of heat-seeking AIM-9 Sidewinders), and it is this weapons configuration that would most likely be employed by F-14s assigned to long-range BarCAP duty.

While it may be the most impressive, Phoenix isn't the only armament option available to the Tomcat and it is possible to mix and match weapons to perform different missions intended to counter specific threats. Reference has already been made to the short-range heat-seeking Sidewinder, but the F-14 is also compatible with the radar-guided AIM-7 Sparrow and its eventual replacement, the AIM-120 Advanced Medium Range Air-to-Air Missile (AMRAAM). Finally, for close-in encounters, the F-14 is fitted with a single multi-barreled Vulcan M61-A1 20mm cannon, so it is clearly able to engage opponents across the entire air-to-air combat spectrum.

As the second element in the fleet defence mission, ForCAP resources operate closer to the Task Force and would carry a mixed bag of armament as they seek to knock out enemy aircraft that succeed in penetrating the BarCAP line. Phoenix is less likely to feature since short-and medium-range missiles are clearly preferable for such eventualities, where combat is likely to be joined at fairly close range. In consequence, either Sparrow or AMRAAM would be the principal missile, with six rounds again being carried, plus the usual pair of Sidewinders. As a last resort, there is the cannon, and

Above: The outer defences of a USN carrier group consists of pairs of F-14 fighters armed with Phoenix missiles, working in conjunction with an E-2C Hawkeye early warning aircraft. In-flight refuelling enables the F-14s to remain on station for up to 3.5 hours.

Right: The F-14 Tomcat has a maximum speed of mach 2.34 and a ceiling of some 60,000ft (18,300m). For 20 years it has been unchallenged as the finest and most powerful carrier-borne fighter in any navy, a position unlikely to change in the near future.

NE
107
107

Left: Carrier operations are a high-risk business; between entering service in 1972 and August 1988 no less than 101 F-14 Tomcats had been lost in accidents. This aircraft came to grief in the crash barrier on board USS *Kitty Hawk* (CV-63), in 1984.

Left Below: The aircraft seen above has been saved by the crash-barrier, her crew have survived and an outbreak of fire was prevented. Now the wreckage is removed by a mobile crane to clear the deck.

Below: As the sun sets over the Persian Gulf the last F-14 Tomcat touches down on USS *Carl Vinson* (CVN-70). Now the aircrews can rest, but the maintenance crews day is just starting.

live firing is a regular feature of the training programme.

Finally, there is TarCAP, and here the weapons configuration adopted will be largely influenced by the proximity of the threat posed by enemy fighters, as well as being dictated to some extent by target location and type and by the rules of engagement that are in force. Again, Phoenix is less likely to be carried, with either Sparrow or AMRAAM and Sidewinder being the preferred weapons. In a "free-fire" situation, however, it is conceivable that all three options could be available, perhaps in a two Phoenix, four Sparrow/AMRAAM and two Sidewinder mix.

One other aspect of the Tomcat does deserve brief mention and this concerns its air-to-ground ability, it perhaps not being widely realised that the F-14 is compatible with conventional general-purpose bombs of the Mk.80 series. At the moment, however, such potential must be viewed as being latent, since aircrew do not routinely practice with such weapons. Recent trials conducted by the Naval Air Test Center at Patuxent River, Maryland, with the F-14 and F-14A+ have included carriage of up to four Mk.83 "thousand-pounders", and it is possible that the training syllabus could be expanded to include a limited amount of "air-to-mud" instruction. Such activities are, of course, only likely to be undertaken in the most permissive of environments, where the air-to-air threat is either non-existent in the first place or has been eliminated by earlier operations.

Two generations removed from the Tomcat but still active in the fleet fighter role is the Chance Vought Crusader,

which was once widely used by front-line USN carrier-borne squadrons for fleet defence, attack and reconnaissance duties. Today, alas, this handsome machine no longer figures in the American military line-up, but limited numbers are still to be found operating at sea, aboard the French carriers *Foch and Clemenceau*.

Barely half of the 42 F-8E(FN) Crusaders that were delivered to the Aeronavale as replacements for the Aquilon (Sea Venom) during the 1960s still survive, but these are expected to continue in service until the navalized Dassault-Breguet Rafale becomes available late in the present decade. Featuring extensive modifications to wing geometry in order to permit it to operate safely from the small French carriers, the F-8E(FN) relies mainly on the locally-manufactured Matra R530 radar-guided missile as its primary air-to-air weapon, backed up by the Matra Magic heat-seeker and a quartet of Colt Mk.12 20mm cannon with roughly 125 rounds of ammunition per gun.

Like the later USN models, Aeronavale Crusaders were ''wired'' for the AGM-12 Bullpup air-to-surface missile although there is no evidence to indicate that this rather ineffectual weapon was ever obtained by France. As a result, while they may in theory have been multi-mission capable, the F-8E (FN)s have always been used in the pure intercept role, leaving responsibility for strike and attack missions to the purpose-built Dassault-Breguet Etendard IV and, at a later date, the Super Etendard.

No such ambiguity exists in the case of the British Aerospace (BAe) Sea Harrier, which definitely possesses dual capability. Although it is clearly best known for its air-to-air exploits during the course of the 1982 battle to retake the Falkland Islands, Sea Harriers assigned to the British Task Force also undertook numerous ground attack missions during the early part of that conflict. Ordnance that was employed included conventional 1,000-lb bombs, cluster bomb units (CBU) and 20mm cannon, and the Sea Harrier demonstrated that it was able to achieve a high degree of accuracy when operating in the attack role.

Following the arrival of a number of RAF Harrier GR.3s, the Sea Harrier contingent thereafter concentrated on the battle for control of the air. This was a battle

Left: A French Navy LTV F-8E (FN) Crusader armed with Magic air-to-air missiles prepares for launch from *Clemenceau*. Note the unique variable incidence wing, which has been raised for take-off. France bought 42 of these excellent fighters in 1966 and a few remain in service.

Above: HMS *Invincible* at sea. Her BAe Sea Harriers are dual-capable and highly effective aircraft. In the 1982 Falklands War Royal Navy Sea Harriers destroyed 23 Argentine aircraft and undertook many ground-attack missions in support of the forces ashore heading for Port Stanley.

Right: BAe Sea Harrier FRS.1 on HMS *Invincible*'s elevator. The RN acquired 42 of these excellent aircraft and the Indian Navy has ordered 24 of the very similar FRS.51, with at leat ten more planned. The US Marine Corps, and the Italian and Spanish navies opted instead for the AV-8A Harrier and AV-8B Harrier II versions.

NAS

Left: Lieutenant D. A. O'Meara, RN, sits in his Sea Harrier FRS.1 awaiting the order to start-up and taxi forward for take-off. V/STOL aircraft make much fewer demands on deck-space and flight deck manpower than conventional aircraft since they do not require catapults; their normal mode of launch being over the ski-jump.

Below: An AV-8A Matador of the Spanish *Arma Aerea de la Armada* (fleet air arm) flies over the carrier *Dedalo*. Spain entered the fixed-wing carrier business in 1976 with this carrier/aircraft combination. Today the carrier is the specially designed, Spanish-built carrier *Principe de Asturias* and the aircraft is the BAe/McDD/EAV-8B Harrier II.

that was never entirely won (there were too few defending fighters available), but the Sea Harrier's presence was of vital importance in ensuring a satisfactory outcome from the British point of view.

No less significant was the principal weapon used by the Fleet Air Arm, and had it not been for American assistance in making the all-aspect AIM-9L Sidewinder missile available, it appears probable that the Task Force would have sustained heavier losses in the face of determined attacks by Argentina's aircrews. As it was, the defending fighters exacted a severe toll, accounting for at least two dozen enemy aircraft in air combat. Although cannon fire was used on a number of occasions, most of the successes that were scored were directly attributable to the trusty Sidewinder. Even more remarkable is the fact that of the six aircraft lost in the South Atlantic, only two were as a result of enemy action and both of those fell foul of ground defences when engaged in attack missions.

At the present time, the Sea Harrier FRS.1 continues to be the mainstay of the Fleet Air Arm's (FAA) two frontline fixed-wing squadrons and a training unit, all of which are shore-based at Yeovilton. Looking to the future, the vastly improved Sea Harrier FRS.2 is expected to begin to enter service in 1992, and this will introduce a radar-missile capability in the shape of the AIM-120A AMRAAM while also retaining the proven Sidewinder. Attack potential is also enhanced, with the FRS.2 able to carry and launch the Sea Eagle air-to-surface anti-ship missile. Other note-worthy changes relate to the radar, with look-down/shoot-down Blue Vixen kit being installed in place of the existing Blue Fox unit.

First flown in prototype form in September 1988, most Sea Harrier FRS.2s will originate from a mid-life weapons system update programme which should result in some three dozen survivors from the original FRS.1 procurement of 57 aircraft being brought up to the new, improved standard. Some new-build machines are to be obtained and 10 are now on order from BAe.

Despite its achievements in the South Atlantic and even though interest was expressed by a number of naval air arms, the Sea Harrier has achieved only modest export success. Indeed, it serves only with the Indian Navy, which utilises the Mk.51 version (basically similar to the FRS.1) from its two carriers, the *Vikrant* and the *Viraat*.

However, other variants of the Harrier are routinely flown from ships at sea by Spain's Aerea de la Armada and the US Marine Corps (USMC), with Italy set to join this elite "club" in the near future. In all three instances, though, it is the AV-8B Harrier II or AV-8B Harrier II Plus that is or will be utilised, predominantly in the light-attack role. Additional avionics kit and compatibility with night vision goggles has expanded this type's potential quite significantly and it is no longer confined to operating only by day. When employed on offensive operations, "smart" and "dumb" bombs may be carried as well as more sophisticated weapons such as Maverick, and the AV-8B also totes the ubiquitous AIM-9 Sidewinder for self-defence.

Another McDonnell Douglas product and one that is solely of US origin serves as a convenient link between the separate

Below: A Sea Harrier makes a vertical landing aboard a British Invincible class carrier. The Sea Harrier and AV-8B Harrier II provide the only economical method by which smaller navies can operate fixed-wing aircraft at sea. Carrier-borne V/STOL has been proven operationally in both the Falklands and Gulf Wars, and is now a thoroughly mature concept.

Left: Commander Mike Anderson, USN, is helped by his deck crewman as he prepares for a launch in his McDonnell-Douglas F/A-18 Hornet. Controversial in its early days, this machine has now proved itself.

Below: In the murk and deafening noise normally associated with flight deck operations a deck crewman guides an F/A-18 Hornet pilot towards the catapult shuttle. The multi-role Hornet is highly capable of most air-to-air and air-to-ground missions.

Below Right: An F/A-18 Hornet is directed on to the catapult by a flight deck director on board the Midway class carrier, USS *Coral Sea* (CV-43). Curiously, this aircraft has been armed with only one wing-tip AIM-9 air-to-air missile.

missions of air superiority and strike/attack. I refer to the McDonnell Douglas F/A-18 Hornet, a type that traces its origins back to a US Air Force contest of the early-1970s for a lightweight air combat fighter. That contest eventually led to the hugely successful F-16 Fighting Falcon, but the losing submission – the Northrop YF-17 – was sufficiently good on its own account to lay the basis for today's Hornet.

The latter is one of the few designs of the modern era that can genuinely claim to possess multi-mission capability in its basic form, for apart from altering the weapons payload, it is only necessary to make minor changes to computer software and to ''bolt-on'' a couple of sensor pods to transform it from being a potent fleet defence fighter into a highly effective ''mud-mover''. Thus, it can fairly be described as a swing fighter and it is this ability to respond to force of circumstance by rapidly changing mission that is perhaps its greatest value to the USN of today.

At the heart of this ability is the Hughes AN/APG-65 multi-mode pulse-Doppler radar which appears to be equally adept in air-to-air and air-to-ground modes, while the new technology multi-function display (MFD) cathode ray tubes and the inevitable head-up display (HUD) unit keep the pilot abreast of the developing tactical situation. The Hornet also makes use of the much-vaunted Hands On Throttle and Stick (HOTAS) philosophy, with switches on the pilot's control column and the throttle lever being conveniently to hand, so that he can rapidly change functions and call up data on the MFD screens. Thus, he is able to spend most of the time flying ''head-up'' (i.e. looking out of the cockpit) which greatly enhances his tactical awareness and reduces the chances of him being ''bounced'' by enemy fighters.

Weapons carried by the Hornet are obviously dictated by the mission that is being performed and, to some extent, by the version that is flown. The initial F/A-18A variant was less versatile in this respect, but the current F/A-18C features revised flight instruments and avionics and is compatible with a wider range of ordnance, all of which, with the exception of the obligatory Vulcan M61-A1 20mm cannon, is carried externally. Both variants possess a total of nine weapons stations, although on all-weather ''mud-moving'' missions two of these stations (located on each engine intake outer wall) would house the special sensor pods mentioned earlier, one being an AN/ AAS-38 Forward-Looking Infra-Red (FLIR) unit and the other a laser spot tracker/strike camera system.

Above: The catapult officer signals to the pilot of an F/A-18 Hornet that all is ready for launching and that the deck personnel are clear. Within seconds the aircraft will be hurtling forwards on another mission.

Below: Air-to-air refuelling gives a significant extension to the F/A-18 Hornet's already formidable range. The US Navy uses the 'probe-and-drogue' refuelling method rather than the 'flying-boom' of the USAF.

In pure air-to-air taskings, Sidewinder and Sparrow or AMRAAM missiles are carried, while in air-to-ground operations, the list of options is considerably greater. Conventional bombs of the Mk.80 family are available in either "slick" or "retard" form, but the place of these "dumb" bombs can be taken by an impressive array of smart munitions, including laser-guided bombs, AGM-62 Walleye electro-optically guided bombs, AGM-65 Maverick air-to-surface missiles and, for anti-ship attack tasks, AGM-84 Harpoon missiles. And, of course, the

F/A-18 is also able to deliver tactical nuclear weapons, the arsenal including devices of the B57 and B61 types.

Last, but by no means least, the Hornet may also undertake the hazardous ''Wild Weasel'' defence-suppression mission, using the AGM-88A High-Speed Anti-Radiation Missile (HARM) and either Rockeye II or BL-755 CBUs to eliminate the threat from enemy missile sites. Indeed, it was the Hornet/HARM combination that played an important part in March 1986, when aircraft from the USS *Coral Sea* struck at missile sites in Libya during Operation ''Prairie Fire''. That attack marked the combat debut of both the fighter and the missile, and the pairing was in action again during the following month, partaking in the ''El Dorado Canyon'' raids on Tripoli and Benghazi. Even as the missile-laden fighters went into battle, other Hornets stood CAP duty.

Turning to specialist attack aircraft, there are half-a-dozen types which may be found aboard aircraft carriers around the world. Foremost amongst these, despite the fact that the basic design is more than 30 years old and has been flown in one form or another by several generations of aircrew, is the Grumman A-6 Intruder. A rather unattractive two-seater (pilot and bombardier/navigator),

Below: A fine shot of an F/A-18 Hornet seconds before its hook is 'trapped' by an arrester wire; at this point it is travelling at about 140 knots. The Hornet is renowned for its excellent handling during carrier operations and particularly for its steadiness during the landing approach.

the Intruder made its combat debut in the early period of the Vietnam War and is truly a battle-hardened veteran, having featured in every military action involving US naval air power since then. With the anticipated replacement – the A-12 Avenger – a victim of cancellation, the Intruder seems set to remain in service for some considerable time to come and, in fact, the USN is increasing the size of its fleet of A-6Es by absorbing aircraft flown by a handful of USMC all-weather attack outfits, which are receiving two-seat F/A-18D Hornets as replacements. This is, perhaps, ironic, since the impetus that led to development of the Intruder arose in the first place from a USMC operational requirement of 1956.

The key to the Intruder's durability rests primarily with the sophisticated equipment that allows it to operate at low level in all sorts of weather conditions with a good pay-load. Miniaturisation of key avionics equipment enabled the design to be updated throughout its service life and the contemporary A-6E is a very much more capable and reliable beast than the original A-6A, with the most visible manifestation of change concerning the undernose Target Recognition Attack Mutli-Sensor (TRAM) turret. First installed on late production Intruders and subsequently fitted to all A-6Es, this steerable turret houses an infra-red sensor for classification and identification of targets, a combined laser ranger and designator device and a laser marked-target detection system.

In conjunction with other sensors such as radar, this package allows the Intruder to perform the interdiction role with every chance of success, armament options including ''dumb' and ''smart'' bombs as well as nuclear weapons and air-to-surface missiles such as the AGM-65 Maverick, AGM-84 Harpoon and AGM-88 HARM. Another important new weapon – first used in the Gulf War with startl-

Below: The end product of all the technology and sophistication is a load of iron bombs, which can only be raised to the attachment points by the combined efforts of six men! Nevertheless, these bombs will be delivered with pin-point accuracy by the Grumman A-6 Intruder, whose first flight was in 1960, before most of these men were born!

Right: The two-seater A-6E Intruder is a doughty and reliable aircraft, whose effectiveness stems from the sophisticated navigation and sensing equipment that allows it to operate in every type of weather condition, whilst carrying a hefty payload. Its maximum speed is only 563kt (1,043km/h), this is sufficient for its precision strike role.

ing success – is the Stand-off Land Attack Missile (SLAM), which can be launched towards a target at distances of around 50 miles (80 km), terminal guidance being accomplished with the aid of a TV sensor in the nose of the missile.

When engaged in close air support (CAS), it is able to tote a load of up to 30 Mk. 82 500 lb (227 kg) bombs some 300 nautical miles and then loiter for an hour before returning to the carrier, but the use of in-flight refuelling would obviously extend combat radius. The Intruder's greatest value though will be in precision attacks against "high-value" targets, ideally accomplished under cover of darkness or bad weather so as to reduce the risk of destruction by opposing defences. In this role, SLAM seems likely to assume ever greater importance.

Two other famous attack aircraft of US origin still fly from flight decks on a regular basis, but one of these should soon disappear altogether while the other is at best of questionable value. The latter is

Above: The Vought A-7E Corsair II has had a long and honourable career as a light strike aircraft with the active US Navy. Currently being replaced by the F/A-18 Hornet, it remains operational with Naval Reserve Units and Air Force National Guard.

Below: An A-6E Intruder at the moment of touchdown on USS *Kity Hawk* (CV-63), having engaged the third wire to score an "OK, Three" in the LCO's log. The lowered leading-edge slates and wing-tip air-brakes help reduce landing speed.

the celebrated A-4 Skyhawk. This began as a carrier-based light attack aircraft but no longer features in the USN's front-line inventory although the two-seat TA-4J has been used to train countless naval aviators over the past two decades.

While it may no longer be used operationally in the country of its creation, the Skyhawk is still an important asset for a number of overseas nations, only one of which routinely uses it at sea. This is Argentina, which acquired 16 A-4Qs in the early 1970s for service with the Commando de Aviacion Naval Argentina (CANA) the aircraft carrier *25 de Mayo*. However, attrition – sustained in both peace and war – has reduced the size of this modest fleet to barely a handful, but these do still fly from Argentina's solitary aircraft carrier from time to time even though their potency is far eclipsed by the Exocet-armed Super Etendard.

Developed as a replacement for USN Skyhawk-equipped light attack squadrons, the Vought A-7 Corsair II is itself now in decline and remains active only with Atlantic Fleet elements, most of which are expected to dispose of it in the very near future. Despite the fact that retirement was fast approaching, the Corsair played its part in "*Desert Storm*" operations to

Overleaf: On board the Argentine Navy's carrier *Vienticinco de Mayo*, where a French-built Super Etendard has just been launched, with another and two A-4 Skyhawks alongside. During the 1982 Falklands War this carrier played little part, although naval pilots showed exceptional bravery in anti-ship operations.

Below: There is some delay in launching these two Navy AIM-9 armed A-7E Corsair IIs from USS *Kitty Hawk* (CV-63), with pilots and deck crew waiting patiently but alertly for clearance to proceed. The nearest aircraft is being flown by Lieutenant "Stormin'" Norman, USN, a nickname made famous in the recent Gulf War by a US Army general.

0757
0662

ARMADA
07
3-A-207
DA
207
3·A·309

liberate Kuwait although its contribution was small when compared with that of the newer generation of carrier-borne warplanes, largely due to the fact that these modern aircraft were present in somewhat greater numbers.

Although it was never the hottest ''ship'' in terms of performance, payload capability was impressive and the definitive A-7E variant was later modified to carry a FLIR pod which allowed it to operate at night or in bad weather. In addition, it was able to utilise ''smart'' weapons of either the electro-optically or laser guided type, as well as ''dumb'' iron bombs. Other update initiatives provided compatibility with HARM and Harpoon for special tasks such as defence-suppression and maritime strike, while it also packed the standard ''punch'' bestowed by a single Vulcan 20mm cannon. In summing up the Corsair, perhaps the greatest tribute that one can pay is to reveal that it was one of the very few USN warplanes that also found its way into the US Air Force inventory in considerable numbers.

Of later vintage, but, like the Corsair, based on an earlier design, the Dassault-

Above: The pilot of a Vought A-7E Corsair II carries out final cockpit checks prior to a carrier launch. He is sitting on a Martin-Baker ejector seat, a device which has saved many airmen's lives.

Below: An A-7E Corsair II from Attack Squadron VA-46 carries out a visual check of the carrier's flight-deck prior to entering the recovery pattern for a landing on his parent ship, USS *Eisenhower* (CVN-69).

Above: A Super Etendard of the French Aeronavale leaves the flight deck of a Clemenceau class carrier. The method of launch on the French carriers uses wire strops rather than attaching the aircraft's nose undercarriage leg to the shuttle by means of a bar. Although normally armed with Exocet ASMs, the Super Etendard has a nuclear strike role.

Breguet Super Etendard is the standard shipboard strike fighter with France's Aeronavale and first gained world prominence when Argentinian examples succeeded in launching Exocet missiles against the British Task Force in 1982. Although it had only a handful of aircraft and missiles, the CANA was able to inflict a substantial amount of damage on the fleet and this undoubtedly exerted considerable influence on subsequent Royal Navy operations and tactics. Later, a few aircraft were leased to Iraq and these also succeeded in wreaking havoc during the war with Iran, most prominently in attacks on oil terminal installations at Kharg Island. Since then, the Super Etendard has avoided the limelight even though it has acquired a potent new weapon in the shape of the Aerospatiale ASMP stand-off nuclear missile.

In reality, of course, the nuclear strike option was present from the outset but would have been far more risky for the Super Etendard and its pilot in so far as the only nuclear weapon available was the AN52 gravity bomb. Turning to conventional attack, the Super Etendard may employ free-fall bombs and unguided 68mm rocket pods as well as a pair of DEFA 30mm cannon, while it has a measure of defensive capability in the shape of the Matra Magic heat-seeking air-to-air missiles. In theory, then, it could be used by the Aeronavale for fleet defence, but that mission continues to be performed by the F-8E(FN) Crusader.

Other carrier-borne resources are far less numerous and are engaged in rather less sexy roles, but one should not think that their contribution is insignificant, for that is far from being the case. Some, like those types engaged on ASW duties, have a potentially aggressive role to play in ensuring security of the fleet – others, like those which fulfil AEW and ECM, might fairly be categorized as "force multipliers".

Foremost amongst ASW-dedicated aircraft is the Lockheed S-3 Viking, which presently serves with about a dozen USN squadrons. Production of new-build Vikings was limited to just 187 S-3As, but an on-going modification project seems likely to result in most of the survivors being updated to S-3B standard, with enhanced acoustic processing capability, a new sonobuoy reference system, improved radar processing and new weaponry. Initial deployment of the S-3B came shortly before the end of the 1980s, and the principal mission remains that of countering the sub-surface threat with torpedoes and depth charges. The Viking can also be used for conventional bombing tasks but a more likely secondary duty is anti-ship attack, where little or no defences are expected, and it is here that the S-3B has an advantage over the earlier model, for it has been "wired" to carry and fire Harpoon.

Once the stalwart of USN fixed-wing carrier-borne ASW outfits, the Grumman S-2 Tracker has long disappeared from that air arm, but some of these veterans are still active with Argentina and Brazil. As already noted, Brazil has recently been forced to retire its aircraft carrier, but Argentina continues to deploy the Tracker aboard the *25 de Mayo* at regular intervals. Both of these operators are subjecting their Trackers to update programmes, with the clearest indication of change concerning a switch from piston to turbine power. Less obvious, but rather more significant, is the concurrent updating of avionics, but the armament is apparently unchanged and still consists of a mix of acoustic homing torpedoes and conventional unguided depth charges.

Of similar vintage and also set to remain operational until the next century is the Aeronavale's Breguet Alize, although this portly aircraft has enjoyed the advantage

Above: Most S-3As are now being upgraded to S-3B standard, which includes new avionics, an advanced radar and wiring for Harpoon ASMs. A special electronic reconnaissance version is also being developed.

Below: A Lockheed S-3 Viking of Anti-submarine Squadron VS-28 takes off from USS *Forrestal* (CV-59). All US carriers operate a squadron of ten of these highly effective aircraft to conduct long-range ASW operations.

Right: Launch sequence for a Breguet Alize ASW aircraft of Indian Navy Air Squadron (INAS) 310. The aircraft is being launched from INS *Vikrant*, but this ship is now having her catapults removed so that a ski jump can be installed. This means that the Alizes will in future operate only from shore bases; but as they have been in service for over twenty years they are now somewhat long in the tooth for carrier operations.

of being turbine-powered throughout its three decades of service. Again, modernization of the sensor suite has bestowed expanded ASW capability and the 30 or so examples that remain from original production of about 75 are to be subjected to yet another life extension programme. Torpedoes and depth charges are the primary weapons, but the Alize can also be called upon to perform anti-ship attack tasks, although these would normally be the domain of the Super Etendard. India's naval air arm also operates a few Alizes but these are now flown only from shore bases, with responsibility for carrier-borne ASW being the province of the Sea King helicopter.

First employed by the USN in the early-1960s, the Sikorsky SH-3 Sea King has been the predominant force in the rotary-wing ASW world ever since and variants are presently active with six of the eight nations with carrier forces, the only exceptions being France (which has always endeavoured to do its own thing) and the USSR. As well as US production, the Sea King has been manufactured under licence by a number of nations, and those which today fly from the flight decks of carriers around the world include British and Italian-built machines.

In USN service, the Sea King is at long last beginning to be replaced by the SH-60F Seahawk, but the SH-3H version is likely to be a familiar sight for a few years yet. Of the other nations, Argentina, India and Spain have yet to reveal any plans for replacement, but both Italy and the UK will, if all goes according to schedule, begin to convert to the EH.101 in the mid 1990s. To be known in Royal Navy service as the Merlin, some of these large, powerful helicopters are slated to be deployed for the ASW role aboard the carriers of both navies.

At the moment, though, the Sea King rules and it relies mainly on torpedoes and depth charges for its punch, although some operators have added an anti-ship attack capability with weapons like the Sea Skua and Sea Eagle. In most cases, the Sea King also performs a secondary plane-guard function, retrieving aircrew from the sea in the event of mishaps during launch or recovery. The British also use a commando assault version.

Moving on to ECM, only one country is in the happy position of being able to

Above: A French Navy Aerospatiale Alouette light multi-purpose helicopter prepares for take-off. Despite the age of the design (first flight was in 1959), many remain in service with navies around the world.

Below: A Royal Navy Westland Sea King approaching an Invincible class carrier. The British firm of Westland has manufactured several hundred of these helicopters under licence from Sikorsky, including many for export.

Right: Royal Navy HAS-5 Sea King anti-submarine helicopters warming-up on the flight deck of an Invincible class carrier, clearly showing the four 'Orange Crop' ESM passive receivers immediately above the tail-wheel.

Left: Sikorsky SH-60B Seahawks are now in service in large numbers, the ASW version replacing the venerable SH-3 Sea King in US Navy service. Besides its ASW capabilities the SH-60B also provides over-the-horizon targeting for ship-launched missiles.

operate specialist equipment and this, not altogether surprisingly, is the United States, which has sufficient Grumman EA-6B Prowlers to permit one squadron to be assigned to each active CVW. Progressive improvement of the AN/ALQ-99 tactical jamming system has greatly enhanced EW capability and these efforts are sure to continue. Thus far, they have led to several "generations" of the Prowler being employed, with each succeeding generation being more capable than the preceding one.

Initially unarmed, the Prowler has now acquired quite a "bite" by virtue of later machines being able to utilize HARM – in theory, this would allow the Prowler to undertake the "Wild Weasel" defence-suppression task, but it is unlikely that such a high-value asset would be employed in this way. Instead, HARM is probably more of a defensive weapon, to be used where the Prowler is itself threatened by enemy surface-to-air missile units.

The latest manifestation is the Advanced Capability (ADVCAP) aircraft, but most of the Prowlers that are now in service are of Improved Capability-2 (ICAP-2) standard. Regardless of sub-type, all are dependent upon pod-mounted transmitters for their EW potential and may be employed in several ways; they can escort friendly strike forces and use their jamming power to degrade enemy defences; undertake stand-off jamming tasks; or play an important role acquiring intelligence pertaining to an enemy's electronic "order of battle". The Prowler is essential for a strike force to successfully attack heavily defended targets.

The only other mission that is routinely

Below: A fine air-to-air shot of a Grumman EA-6B Prowler of Tactical Electronic Warfare Squadron VAQ-140 overflying USS *Eisenhower* (CVN-69). On the outboard pylons are two ALQ-99 tactical jamming pods, powered by windmill generators.

performed from aircraft carriers is that of AEW and, inevitably, it is the USN which leads the field. Its standard AEW asset is the Grumman E-2C Hawkeye, with current production machines relying on AN/APS-139 radar as the primary sensor. Updating of processor equipment allows it to cope with over 2,000 target tracks, but overland detection capability is to be improved still further with adoption of General Electric's AN/APS-145 radar.

While the Hawkeye's primary responsibility is that of detecting threats to the Task Force and Carrier Battle Group, it may also function as an Airborne Command and Control System (ACCS) and can be used for surface surveillance duties. In the latter role, the Hawkeye's radar extends coverage available to the parent carrier and, in turn, offers greater warning of and reaction time to hostile shipping and low-flying aircraft or missiles. Similar duties are now undertaken by suitably-modified Sea King helicopters that serve with the naval air arms of the United Kingdom

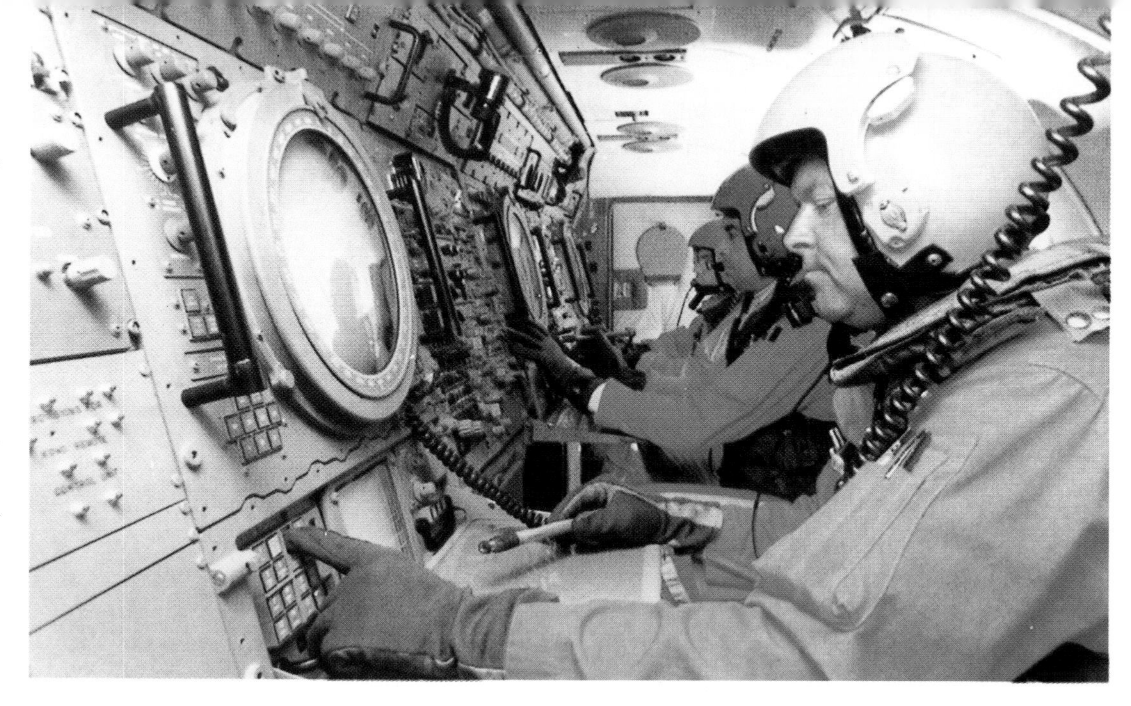

Above: Inside a Grumman E-2C Hawkeye airborne early warning aircraft, with the air control officer (ACO) nearest the camera. The APS-125 radar can detect aircraft at ranges of up to 240nm (444km) and can track up to 250 air and sea targets.

Below: An E-2C Hawkeye touches down. Its radome is 24ft (7.3m) in diameter and rotates six times per minute. The height to the top of the radome is 18.33ft (5.6m) but the mounting can be lowered for hangar storage, for a height of 16ft (4.87m).

and Spain, both of which rely on Searchwater radar.

Deliberately left to last, since it is very much an unknown quantity, is the Soviet Union, which is now on the brink of acquiring a large-deck carrier force to augment the quartet of *Kiev*-class warships. The latter are reasonably small vessels but do feature a mix of fixed-wing aircraft and helicopters in their embarked air groups. The mainstay of fixed-wing resources is the Yakovlev Yak-38 ''Forger'' V/STOL fighter, with a typical complement at sea consisting of a dozen single-seat ''Forger-As'' and a couple of two-seat ''Forger-Bs''. With four underwing stores stations, the ''Forger'' can operate with either air-to-air or air-to-surface weaponry, up to a maximum payload of about 3.5 ton (3,600 kg), but one must question how effective it would be if it came up against modern Western equipment.

Looking ahead, the same design bureau is developing a new warplane for naval service with the designation Yak-41. Presently known to NATO as ''Ram-T'' (an allusion to the Ramenskoye test centre, where it is under development), this is apparently a supersonic V/STOL air defence fighter and is expected to take the place of the ''Forger'' aboard the *Kiev*-class carriers.Still more startling, though, are the prospects for the *Admiral Kuznetsov*, a large carrier which is scheduled to commission some time during 1991. Sea trials have involved suitably modified versions of the MiG-29 ''Fulcrum'', Su-25 ''Frogfoot'' and Su-27 ''Flanker'', and it appears that ''Fulcrum'' and ''Flanker'' may well feature in the embarked Air Wing when this potentially very capable warship deploys operationally for the first time. Between them, they should result in *Kuznetsov* being able to pack a formidable punch. Other carrier-borne hardware consists of helicopters from the Kamov bureau, with variants of the Ka-25 ''Hormone'' and Ka-27/29 ''Helix'' being used for ASW, missile guidance, SAR and assault transport duties. *Kiev*-class vessels normally carry about 15 heli-copters and some seem certain to be present aboard *Kuznetsov* and other members of the class when they become available.

Above: For years Western experts were convinced that the Yak-38 Forger could only take-off vertically and could not perform short, rolling take-offs. This photograph most definitely gives the lie to that assertion.

Below: A Sukhoi Su-27 Flanker lands on the latest Soviet carrier, *Kuznetsov*. The Soviets have chosen to use conventional arrester-gear for landing, but a skijump for take-off rather than install steam catapults.

Right: A ceremonial parade aboard a Soviet Kiev class carrier, with a Kamov Ka-25 Hormone-B in the foreground and a Kamov Ka-27 Helix-D search-and rescue helicopter at the stern. A Don-class command tender/logistic support vessel stands-off.

6

Self-defence

AS noted in Chapter Two, the design of an aircraft carrier, like that of any surface warship, is inevitably the result of a number of compromises. The carrier must be able to accommodate the necessary aircraft, manpower, weapons, sensors, fuel and machinery, maintenance workshops, and living and recreation facilities to fulfil the mission. Furthermore, it must be capable of allowing these assets to be used effectively in the combat environment and weather conditions stipulated by the naval staff in the initial operational requirement. Not surprisingly, the largest single element is the Air Wing and the scale of the requirement can be comprehended when it is apreciated that in the US Navy's Nimitz class, the aviation-related payload (aircraft, ordnance, support facilities, fuel, manpower, etc) comes to no less than 15,000 tons (18,288 tonnes) including 88 aircraft and 3,626 officers and ratings.

Current US Navy philosophy is that what really matters are sheer numbers of aircraft, accompanied by the maximum amount of fuel and weapons. In addition, each carrier must accommodate a balanced Air Wing in order to give the Carrier Task Group maximum tactical self-sufficiency and survivability, with sufficient aircraft to carry out and sustain its particular mission. Previous chapters have dealt with aircraft carriers in their aviation role; this chapter deals with aircraft carriers as fighting vessels in their own right.

The question of the optimum weapons fit for aircraft carriers has exercised naval staffs and designers for years. However, there now appears to be something of a consensus that aircraft carriers need have only minimal close-in (or ''last-ditch'') protection and rely for the rest on their aircraft and the other ships in the Task Group. In the 1950s and 1960s, most aircraft carriers were armed with between eight and twelve medium-calibre, dual-purpose guns; for example, HMS *Eagle* mounted eight 4.5in guns, while the USS *Forrestal* mounted eight 5in Mk 42 guns. In both cases these were intended primarily for short-range air defence, although with a secondary last-ditch surface capability, if required.

More recently, the US Navy's aircraft carriers have had their medium-calibre gun armaments totally removed. The standard weapons fit now comprises a mix of Sea Sparrow surface-to-air missiles (SAMs) and Mark 15 20mm Vulcan/Phalanx automatic close-in weapons systems (CIWS).

It was the ever-innovative Soviet Navy that broke the pattern with their Moskva and Kiev class designs. In these ships the entire forward area is devoted to weaponry, with a mixture of guns, missiles and anti-submarine warfare (ASW) rocket launchers. However, the Moskva class, with its large superstructure and after flight-deck, operates only helicopters. In the Kiev class both helicopters and Yak-38 ''Forger''

Right: USS *Eisenhower* (CVN-69) launches a Sea Sparrow SAM. Modern US carriers depend upon their aircraft and other ships in the carrier task group for protection and only carry 'last-ditch' weapons. *Eisenhower* mounts three Mark 29 launchers, each with eight Sea Sparrows, plus three 20mm Vulcan/Phalanx CIWS.

VTOL fighters operate from its angled deck, with the entire forecastle devoted to a mixture of weapons; but it appears that this has caused airflow problems and turbulence over the flight-deck and steps have had to be taken to alleviate this. These have included removing the port 30mm gatling gun sponson from its position forward of the flight-deck and fitting wind-deflection plates just abaft the SS-N-12 surface-to-surface missile (SSM) launchers.

The latest Kuznetsov class is of a more conventional design with its island offset to starboard, but is still heavily armed in comparison with Western aircraft carriers, with 16 SS-N-19 SSM launchers in addition to its medium- and short-range SAM systems. However, the new systems are all mounted in vertical-launch magazines inset into the decks, so there is no large-scale use of deck-space, and the associated airflow problems of the earlier designs have been avoided. The Soviets' large new super-carrier *Ul'yanovsk* will be similarly armed.

The Italian Garibaldi class are comparatively heavily armed for their size, with four Otomat-Teseo SSM launchers

Above: Shown on *Kiev*'s foredeck are: two MBU-4500 ASW rocket-launchers (A); twin-arm SUW-N-1 anti-submarine missile launcher (B); twin 76mm DP gun turret (C); eight tubes for SS-N-12 long-range SSM (D); SA-N-3 Goblet SAM launcher (E); three 23mm Gatling CIWS turrets (F); and a retractable SA-N-4 short-range SAM launcher (G).

Below: One of the most successful weapons systems of the 1980s is the Vulcan/Phalanx 20mm Gatling CIWS, which is mounted on all modern US Navy aircraft carriers. There are two radars, one of which follows the incoming missile and the other the projectile stream. A computer reduces the difference between the two to zero, thus ensuring target destruction.

situated on the quarterdeck giving them an effective anti-ship capability. There are also two eight-cell Albatros SAM launchers, mounted fore and aft of the island, together with six 40mm anti-aircraft (AA) guns. Surprisingly, these ships also mount two sets of triple torpedo launchers, although it is difficult to foresee the tactical circumstances in which these triple launchers might be used.

Today's smaller aircraft carriers tend to follow US practice, with a mixture of medium- and short-range missiles and a cannon-based CIWS. The French *Charles de Gaulle*, for example, will be armed with two 16-missile launchers for SAAM, two Sadral SAM launchers and eight 20mm cannon. The British Invincible class vessels have a Sea Dart launcher on the forecastle and three Dutch Goalkeeper 30mm CIWS. The lightest armament of all is on the Spanish carrier *Principe de Asturias*, which has just two Meroka 20mm CIWS mounts, each of which has only a limited arc of fire since they are located on the quarterdeck.

The aircraft carrier's machinery must be sufficiently powerful not only to provide the required cruising and maximum speeds, but also to give the shortest possible time to accelerate from cruise to flak speed in order to launch aircraft at short notice. On nuclear aircraft carriers the reactors need no fuel, the cores on the latest types being good for some 800,000nm to 1,000,000 (1,482,560km to 1,853,200km) steaming, which is about 13 years of usage. In contrast, the fossil-fuel aircraft carriers must allocate a large amount of storage space to fuel, to the detriment of other commodities.

Aircraft carriers are vulnerable to attack from missiles, bombs, shells and torpedoes, and the passive protection of their hulls has always been a major consideration. Just before the Second World War, the British became the first to use armoured flight-decks, a practice which was vindicated in the Pacific theatre at the end of the war when Japanese *kamikaze* pilots made US and British aircraft carriers their principal targets. However, after the war physical protection was given a lower priority for many years, although protection against nuclear fallout, and against chemical and biological weapons (NBC) led to the creation of ''citadels''.

The threat from submarine-launched torpedoes is particularly severe and US Navy aircraft carriers, in particular, incorporate extensive compartmentalization to combat such a threat. The Forrestal class, for example, have transverse bulkheads below the waterline at 33ft (10m) intervals, with two longitudinal bulkheads stretching vertically from keel to waterline and running from stem to stern: the result is no less than 1,200 watertight compartments. The later Nimitz class has over 2,000 such watertight compartments.

In US carriers the decks and hull are constructed of extra-strong, high-tensile steel to limit the effects of semi-armour-piercing bombs. In addition, since observing the British experiences in the Falklands War, sensitive areas (eg, command-centres) are being given further protection using Kevlar. In a supercarrier such as the USS *Nimitz*, extensive damage-control precautions are taken, with no less than thirty teams on standby at all times; and a 15deg list can be corrected in just 20 minutes.

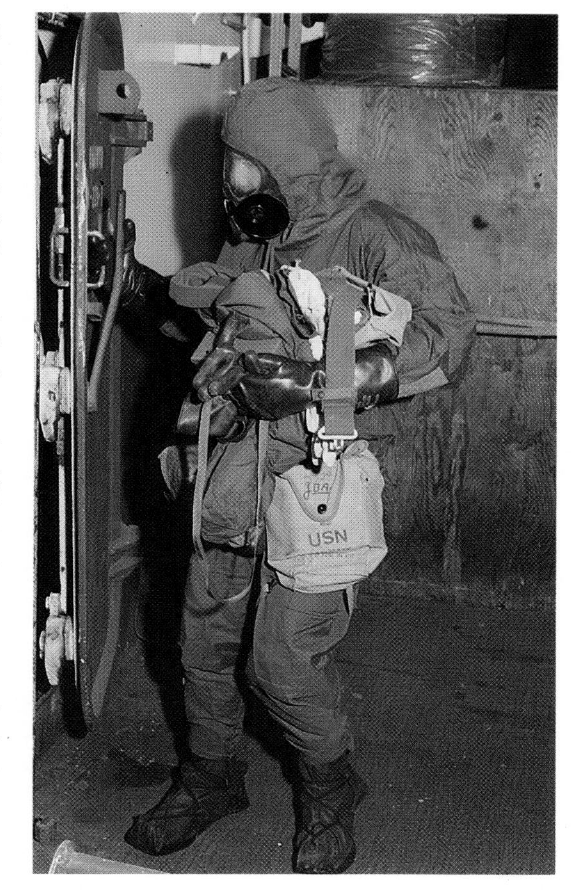

Above: A crewman aboard USS *Forrestal* (CV-59) in full NBC suit during Exercise Teamwork in 1988. In January 1991 such US sailors were wearing their NBC suits during the Gulf War, fully expecting a chemical attack.

Below: A damage-control team aboard USS *Independence* (CV-62) during the Gulf War. Aircraft carriers possess awesome firepower making them prime targets in any conflict, but Iraqi forces never got near Allied warships in either the Red Sea or the Gulf.

Hangar design is crucial to the successful use of the carrier. The hangar itself forms a girder which provides the greatest strength member in the hull, while its internal design and layout affects the number of aircraft that can be carried and also the protection afforded to the overall design. The hangars on US aircraft carriers are huge: on the latest US designs they are some 25ft (7.62m) high. Apart from accommodating the aircraft, however, there are numerous other requirements for space. On Nimitz class carriers, for example, aircraft maintenance workshops now occupy virtually the whole of the space in the huge, port-side sponson supporting the flight deck, while at the after end of the hangar is a large aero-engine shop.

The size and shape of the hangar is even more critical in the smaller aircraft carriers. In the British Invincible class, the original hangar was a "dumb-bell" shape with large areas at either end, but with the middle constricted by the exhaust uptakes for the gas-turbine engines on the starboard side. When the ships were envisaged as ASW helicopter carriers this did not matter too much, but it became a serious limitation when it was decided to embark Sea Harriers as well.

Above: Royal Navy Sea Harrier FRS.1 in the hangar of an Invincible-class aircraft carrier. Note the folding nose radome and the stores stowed along the walls. The hangar is on one level only and consists of three bays, the midships bay being narrower to permit the passage of the exhaust trunking, giving the hangar an overall 'dumb-bell' shape.

Below: US Navy Boeing-Vertol HH-46A Sea Knight transport helicopter picking-up special stores for an underslung lift from USS *John F. Kennedy* (CV-67). Helicopters have proved invaluable at sea for such tasks, being able to transfer relatively large and heavy loads between ships quickly and efficiently in almost any weather, day and night.

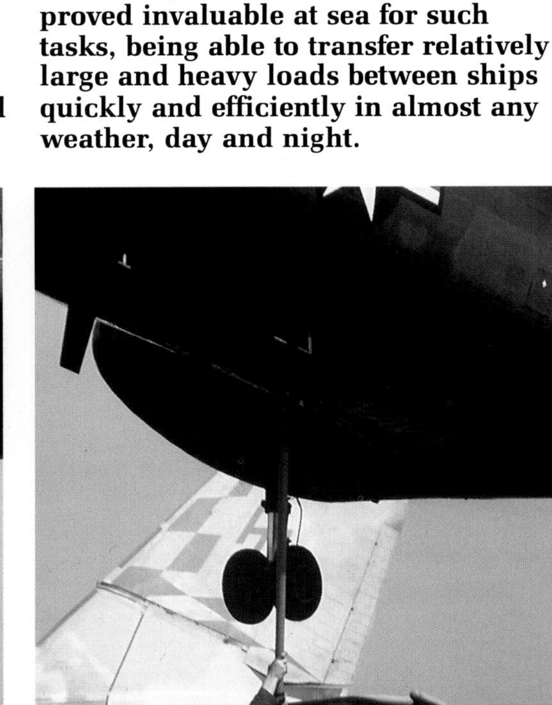

The optimum solution for aircraft stowage is that all should be fitted into the hangar. However, the US Navy long since abandoned this goal, and modern carrier hangars can only accommodate a maximum of about 40 per cent of an Air Wing, the remainder being left exposed to the elements on the flight-deck. Virtually all other Navies now follow suit.

The logistical aspects of looking after the Air Wing, a large ship and an enormous complement are daunting. The nuclear-powered USS *Nimitz* (CVN-68), for example, carries no less than 11,000 tons (11,176 tonnes) of aviation fuel, sufficient for 16 day's operations. It also has 49,652sq ft (15,134m²) of aviation magazine facilities, which can accommodate no less than 1,954 tons (1,985 tonnes) of ordnance. Finally, the needs of the ship itself must be met, not least those of the 6,286 crew members, who must be fed and supplied with water and all of the other life-sustaining commodities.

Aircraft carriers are fitted with a plethora of electronic systems, among the most important of which are the sensors whose antennae can be seen festooned on their islands. Soviet ships are well known for their rich and varied crop of antennae, which are primarily required because Soviet electronic equipment is currently less flexible and sophisticated than equipment produced in the West.

But US Navy ships carry more systems than meet the eye, and the latest, the USS *Theodore Roosevelt*, is a good example. The first and most elementary of her needs is for navigation at sea, for which she carries a Furuno 900 system and a Raytheon SPS-64, the latter an X-band system which can track 20 surface targets at ranges of up to 48nm (89km). For long-range surface search she carries the SPS-67(v), which normally operates in the C-band, but which also has an ultra-short pulse mode for navigation.

Primary air search equipment is the SPS-48C, a three-dimensional (3-D) system which employs electronic frequency scanning. This is backed up by a pair of two-dimensional systems: the SPS-48C for long-range and the SPS-65 for low altitude air search. The carrier must also, of course, be capable of guiding its aircraft back to base and assisting them in land-

Above: The superstructure of a British Illustrious-class carrier. The single large radome at the after end houses the antenna for the Type 909 missile control radar, while the two smaller white domes cover the antennas for a satellite communications system.

Below: Inside the command centre of a British carrier, where all the ship's systems are monitored and controlled. In war, the captain would fight his battle from here, since he will have far more information at his fingertips than on the bridge.

ing: these needs are met by the URN-25 Tactical Air Navigation (TACAN) system and the SPN-43A, -44 and -45 radars for guidance and Instrument Landing System (ILS) approaches. Latest to be fitted is the new SPN-46, sensor which is a vital part of the Automatic Carrier Landing System (ACLS).

For fire control, the USS *Theodore Roosevelt* has one Mk 91 Mod 1 fire director for each of the three Sea Sparrow SAM launchers. The only other weapons available – the four Mk 15 Phalanx 20mm CIWS – each have their own integrated Mk 90 fire control systems.

Above: The air traffic control centre aboard a US Navy aircraft carrier. Control of the carrier's 80-odd aircraft can be quite a problem and at peak periods traffic is much more intense than at land-based airfields.

Most of the electronic warfare (EW) sensors are classified, but among those known to be mounted are the WLR-8(v)4 radar warning system and the SLQ-17 jammer array, which creates false targets to confuse and mislead incoming missiles. Enemy missile guidance systems are also confused by the USS *Theodore Roosevelt's* Mk 36 Super Rapid Blooming Offboard Chaff (SRBOC) system, which consists of four six-tube mortars firing chaff-dispensing cartridges which burst above the ship.

These electronic devices produce such a vast amount of information that they must be integrated by yet more electronic devices: the Naval Tactical Data System (NTDS). This uses digital computers to present the overall picture of the tactical situation covering the air, surface and subsurface plots, thus enabling the Captain to optimise the use of the systems at his disposal to defeat the enemy. Automated digital communications links enable data to be exchanged at high rates with other

Left: Aboard USS *Ranger* (CV-61) two officers assess the display on an AN/UYA-4 weapon-control system. This display shows incoming, high-threat, low-flying weapons, particularly cruise and deep-diving missiles.

NTDS-equipped ships and also with Lockheed P-3C Orion, Grumman E-2C Hawkeye and Lockheed S-3A/B Viking aircraft, which are fitted with the equivalent aircraft-mounted Airborne Tactical Data System (ATDS).

Also installed in the USS *Theodore Roosevelt* is an Anti-Submarine Classification and Analysis Centre (ASCAC), which maintains links with similar facilities at the shore-based Fleet HQ using satellite communications, and with other ASCACs afloat. It also has communications links with airborne ASW aircraft and escorting ships in the Battle Group. This enables a comprehensive plot to be maintained, which displays and analyses all submarine contacts over a very large area of ocean.

In addition to all these sensors there is a multiplicity of communications systems. There are satellite links to the USA, other Fleets and to aircraft such as the Boeing E-4B Advanced Airborne National Command Post (AABNCP). Communications between ships in the same Battle Group are conducted via Ultra-High Frequency (UHF) or Very High Frequency (VHF) wavelengths, although satellite communications can also be used to contact suitably-equipped ships. Communications with the carrier's own aircraft are via UHF and VHF, with High Frequency (HF) wavelengths available as a stand-by or for use at long ranges. HF is also used to receive and re-transmit broadcasts passing general information. Last, but by no means the least important, there are Low Frequency (LF) links to submerged submarines.

The shape of the hull is also extremely important, as it is for any ship. But for their specialized function aircraft carriers need to have minimum pitch and roll to guarantee optimum conditions for the pilots during launch and (particularly) recovery. In addition, the flight-deck must not be so close to the water as to become hazardous for aircraft operations; nor must it be so high as to create serious wind-resistance problems when manoeuvring the ship. The flight-deck of today's US Navy supercarriers is some 93ft (28.36m) above the waterline, which is considerably more advantageous than the Soviet Kiev class 43ft (13m).

Right: The scene aboard a US carrier as specialists review the information provided by computer-driven displays, showing information received from many sources, including ships, submarines, aircraft and satellites.

Below: Despite all the advanced technology, there is still a need for simple, old-fashioned weapons handled by a properly trained and well-motivated crew. These two sailors man a .50in (12.6mm) machine-gun aboard a US Navy carrier during the Gulf War, ready for close-range defences.

The composition of a Carrier Battle Group will vary according to the mission, the resources available and the nature of the threat. In addition to the aircraft carrier, the Group requires escort vessels specializing in the air defence and ASW missions, together with at least one replenishment ship. Groups could also include one or more nuclear-powered attack submarines (SSNs) in support and possibly an additional ASW helicopter carrier.

All tactics are based on the concept of defence in depth, beginning with an outer battle conducted as far from the Carrier Battle Group as possible, where – ideally – the threat itself, whether ship, submarine or aircraft, will have been destroyed before it can compute a weapon launch solution. Should this prove impossible, however, the process of attrition of the threat will then continue through successive combat regions, with engagement of the approaching enemy aircraft or missiles taking place in each so that, should they ever manage to fight their way through to the Inner Point-Defence Zone, they will have been reduced to such an extent that the close-in defensive systems can deal with them.

The first line of air defence is the responsibility of the carrier's fighters. Normally a minimum of two aircraft will be placed on Combat Air Patrol (CAP) at least 100nm (185km) down the line of the enemy's most probable direction of attack. Control of such CAPs will normally be exercised by either an AEW aircraft, by a forward-deployed radar defence picket ship, or by the carrier itself.

Early warning of air attack is vital and modern technology makes a whole host of means available, including military intelligence reports, satellite surveillance, AEW aircraft, CAPs and radar picket ships positioned ahead of the fleet. Of these sources, the first two usually provide accurate and useful information, but are unlikely to give warning with sufficient speed once an enemy attack is underway. AEW aircraft on the other hand are invaluable. For example, a US Navy E-2C Hawkeye aircraft, flying at a height of 30,000ft (9,150m) provides radar

Above: A US Navy carrier task group, with its escort of Ticonderoga class cruisers and Charles F. Adams class destroyers. The airpower projected by such a force makes the aircraft carriers prime targets, so effective air, surface and ASW defence systems are absolutely essential.

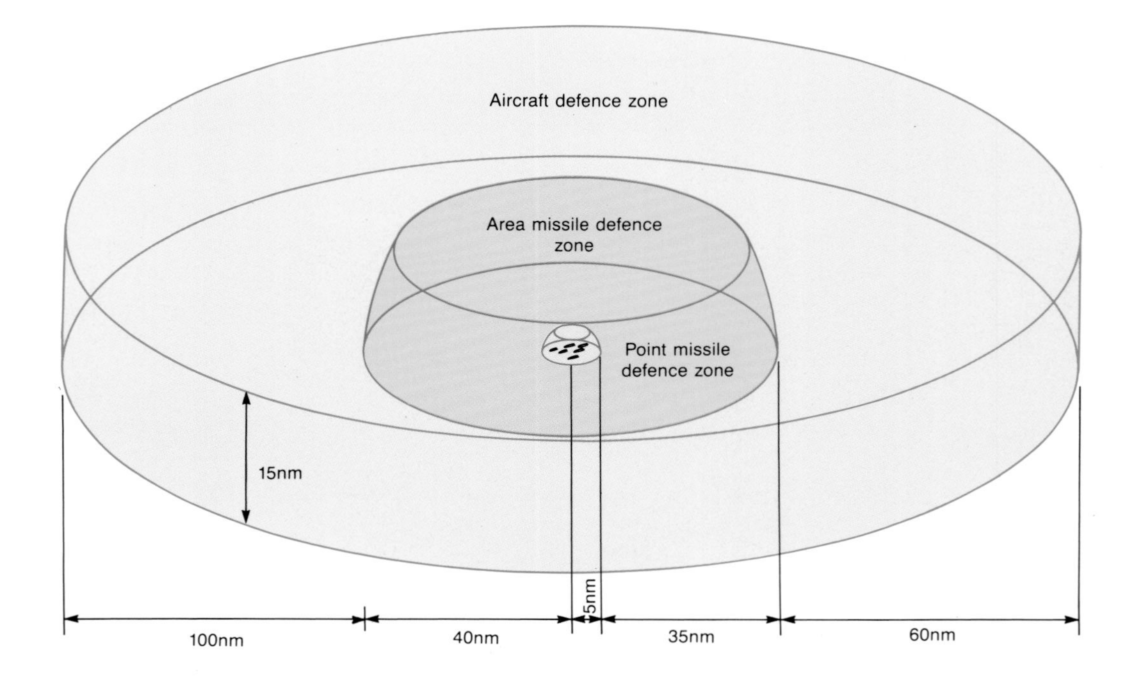

Left: The air defence mission in a carrier group is to destroy the enemy as far away as possible; ideally before missiles can be launched. So, the group would move inside an air defence zone some 100nm (185km) deep, with area and point defence zones to give terminal protection from missiles.

coverage out to 260nm (482km); it can also track up to 800 targets and control up to 40 intercepts simultaneously.

A radar picket ship can also be used to extend a Fleet's radar horizon. This task calls for ships equipped with long-range, high-definition radar, which can be positioned at or near the Carrier Battle Group's radar horizon in the general direction of the expected threat. However, as the sinking of HMS *Coventry* demonstrated in the 1982 Falklands War, such a role is extremely hazardous for the isolated and unprotected picket ship.

The role of the CAP is to seek to destroy both enemy reconnaissance aircraft before they can detect the Fleet and strike aircraft before they can launch their missiles. But, if the attacking aircraft are able to approach at low level and fire their missiles while still below the defending ships' radar patterns, there may be little or no time for a successful fighter interception. Indeed, in the worst case it may be that the incoming attack may not have been detected in time to launch a fighter response. In such a situation, the second line of defence, the Area-Defence Missile Zone, may be the first area in which an indication is given of the approach of the enemy strike force.

Finally, in the Inner Point-Defence Zone itself, individual ships are responsible for their own protection, although escorts can be positioned close alongside others (such as aircraft carriers) to provide mutual defence. Point defence systems such as the British Sea Wolf SAM, the US Navy's Mk 15 Phalanx CIWS, the French Navy's Crotale SAM, and various decoys must be closely coordinated to ensure last-ditch protective cover.

Above: An essential element in the carrier group's air defence screen is airborne early warning, which, in the case of the US Navy is provided by the Grumman E-2C Hawkeye. The 24ft (7.32m) diameter radome houses the APS-125 radar antenna.

Below: Carrier groups also require close-in, rapid reaction air defence systems, usually a mix of missiles for short-range defence and guns for last-ditch protection. This is the latest vertical-launch version of the British Sea Wolf SAM.

When considering the response of a Carrier Battle Group to an air attack it is essential to remember that the enemy almost invariably formulates his firing solution using radar, and is thus unlikely to have been able to positively indentify his target, while the Task Force's defence relies on counter-attack and, perhaps more importantly, deception.

Effective command-and-control (C^2) of these defensive zones is essential, not only to make the best use of the resources, but also to avoid shooting down friendly aircraft (a ''blue-on-blue'') engagement). For example, during the excitement of an air-to-air engagement friendly aircraft could, on occasions, infringe another zone, and if there was any confusion on the command's local air picture plot, this could, all too easily, lead to the force accidentally engaging them. Further, aircraft cannot remain on CAP indefinitely and new aircraft must deploy and the relieved aircraft return, both groups having to transit through the missile defence zones. Strict procedural rules must be imposed to ensure this is done in safety, one possible method being the creation of narrow, missile-tight lanes.

Electronic Warfare (EW) plays a significant part in the air battle, providing target inputs to SAM systems and vectors to defending intercepting aircraft. EW can also degrade enemy air targeting, as well as provide the electronic decoys to counter homing missiles. Jamming the electronic deception of any enemy acquisition radar will force the enemy pilot to approach his target much nearer than he would otherwise wish, making him more likely to encounter the air defence umbrella and thus increasing the chance of his destruction, with his weapons still on their racks.

Deception, and the confusion it can cause either in the mind of an attacking

Right: A good example of inter-Service cooperation as a USAF Boeing KC-135R of Strategic Air Command refuels two Grumman F-14A Tomcats. The USAF tanker's refuelling boom is fitted with a special adaptor to enable it to refuel naval aircraft, which normally use the 'probe-and-drogue' hose system.

Left: Grumman F-14D Tomcat, the USN primary fleet defence fighter. Armed with the Hughes AIM-54 Phoenix missile, the F-14 provides the fleet with an all-weather air defence against supersonic missile and aircraft targets from sea-level to 100,00ft (30,500m).

pilot or in the homing device of a missile, is an essential aspect of maritime defence. Radar detection is the primary – and often the only – means of pinpointing the intended target.

The incoming enemy pilot, flying at high speed and low level, has to identify which of the many contacts he can see on his radar is his designated priority. He perceives the surface force in only two dimensions, but the disposition of the ships is fairly easily discerned and he expects to see a large target, such as an aircraft carrier, at the centre of several smaller contacts. If he is approaching at such low level that he has to increase height momentarily in order to obtain a radar picture of his target, then he must make very quick decisions on the identity of the carrier. So, one of the possibilities available to the naval Commander is to deploy his ships in an unorthodox pattern. For example, the carrier can be placed in the screen itself and another, more expendable vessel put in the centre as a decoy.

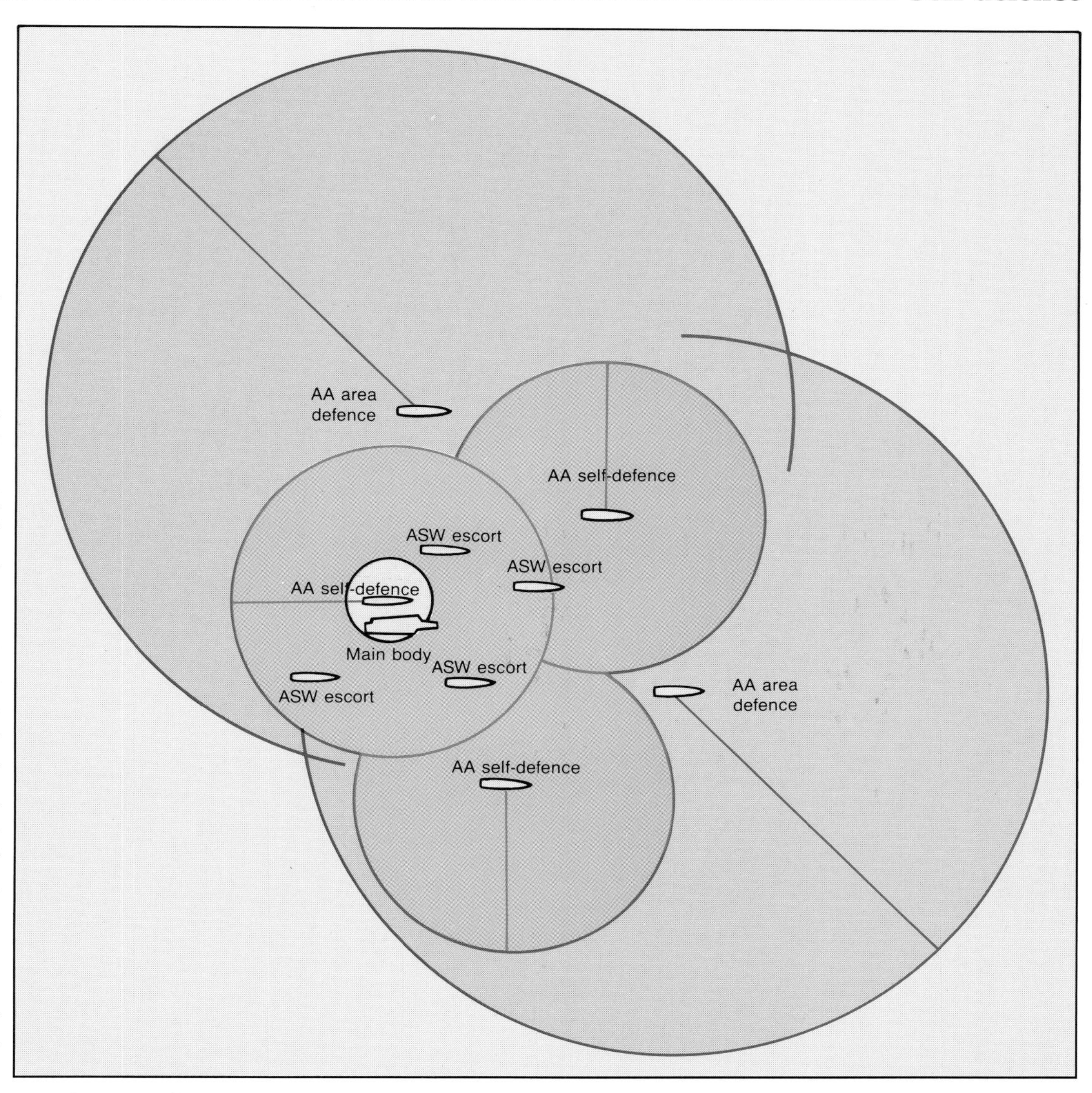

Above: The main body of this task force is a carrier with an escorting cruiser, the latter using its point defence systems (guns, short-range missiles, CIWS) to supplement those of the carrier. Further out, beyond the screen of the ASW escorts, are air defence ships with medium-range and area defence SAM systems to provide defence in depth.

Left: On board USS *Independence* (CV-62) during the Gulf War, with large, blue, computer-generated displays showing the Straits of Hormuz and ship positions. The two smaller screens give information on the individual ships and their status while the third small screen shows actual locations.

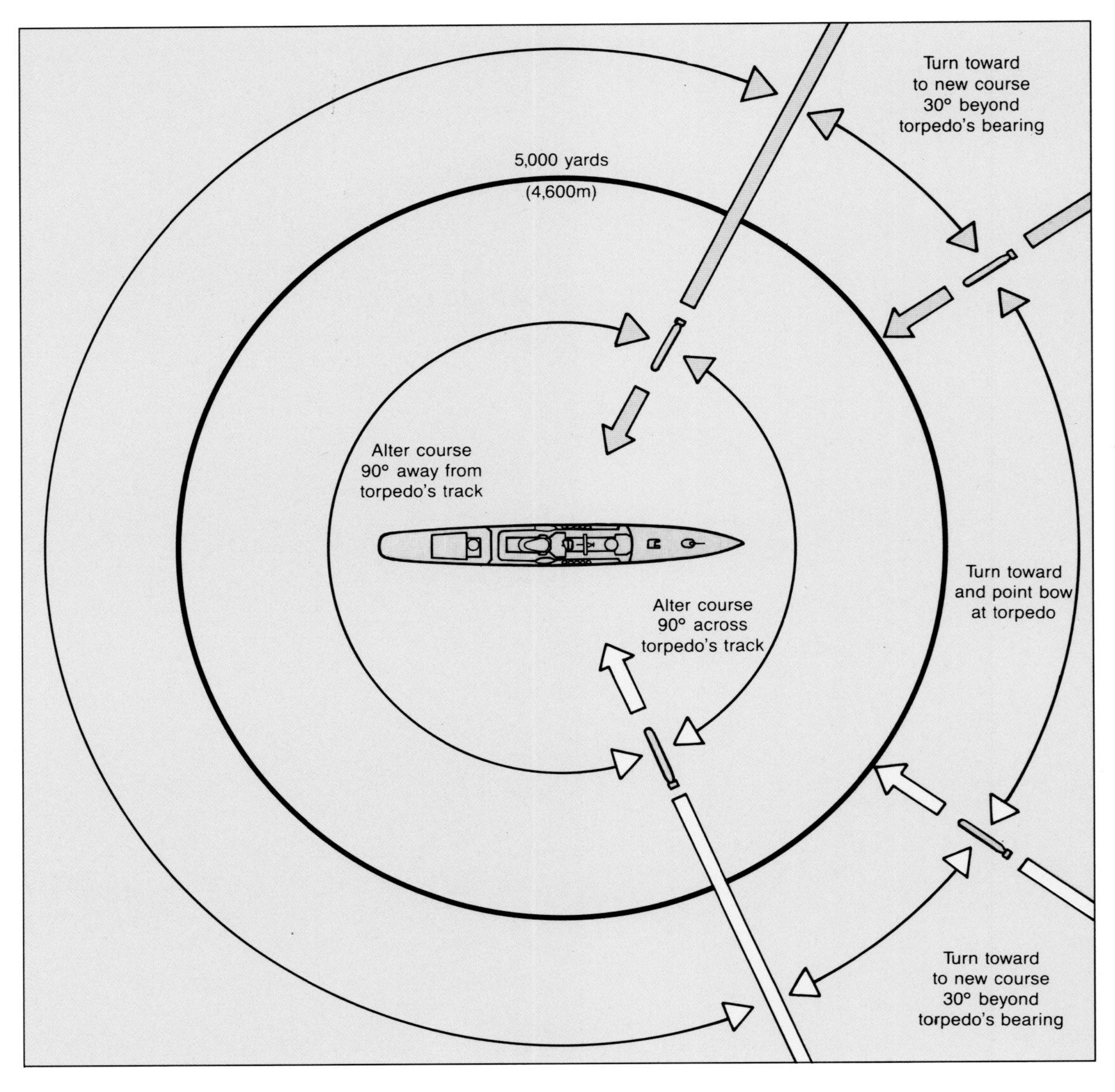

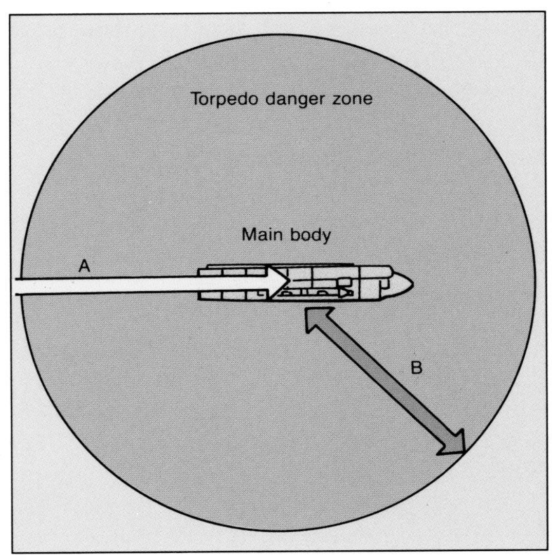

Above: ASW plots are based on the Torpedo Danger Zone (TDZ). An advanced position is calculated based on the centre of the group, allowing for a torpedo's running time (A). Around this is drawn a circle (B), whose radius is the range at which torpedoes would be fired.

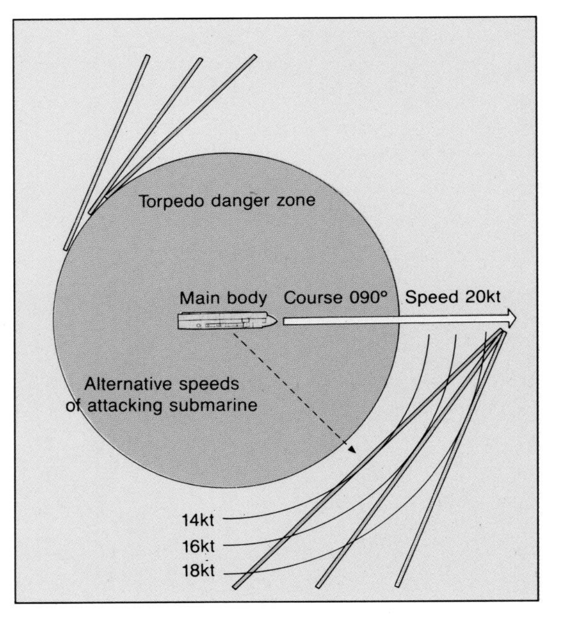

Above: In practice the diagrams Above and Above right are combined, and the relative courses of the submarine, depending upon its speed, plotted. Thus, in this example, a detected submarine with an estimated speed of less than 18 knots and a position to the right of the relative course drawn represents a threat.

Above: When an incoming torpedo is detected immediate action must be taken, as depicted in this diagram, although the response required varies if first detection occurs at under 5,000yd (4,600m). Recent developments in torpedo technology are starting to make evasion by surface ships increasingly difficult.

One of the methods of dealing with missiles is to present them with a phantom target, which can be produced either by the use of chaff or by EW. The US Navy's SLQ-17, for example, which is installed on US Navy supercarriers, produces just such an "offset" target. Jamming on an attacker's radar frequency can deny him essential information, particularly on range. In a similar manner a missile's acquisition radar can be jammed, although once a missile has "locked-on" it is normally extremely difficult to deceive it.

There is much talk of using "stealth" technology at sea, in order to counter enemy radar and infra-red devices. Some sucess is being achieved with smaller vessels, while the rounding of edges, avoidance of reflective "holes" and reductions in the ship's infra-red signature do have some beneficial effect. It does seem rather unlikely, however, that such a huge target as an aircraft carrier could be totally disguised using such methods.

The Carrier Task Group must also defend itself against attack by submarines. As with air defence, the area around the Group is divided into zones, with most, but by no means all, activity oriented towards the most likely directions from

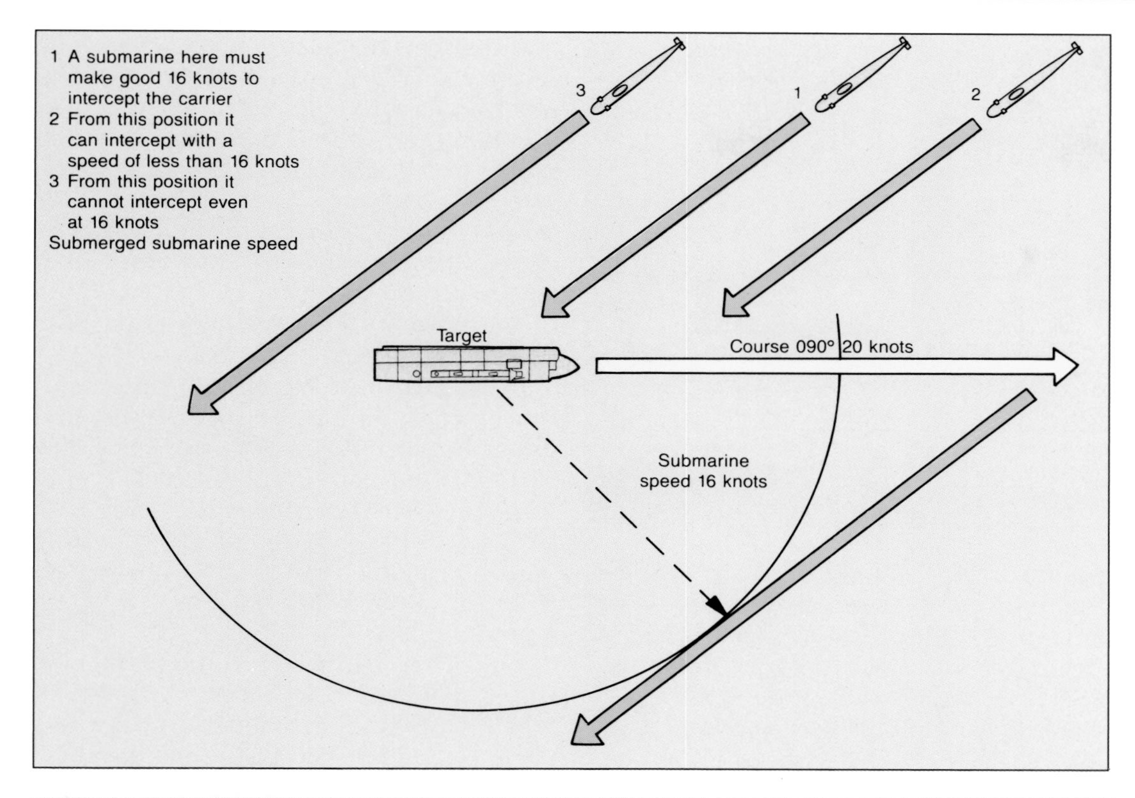

Left: Assuming the submarine's speed to be 16 knots, an arc with this speed as its radius is drawn and the main body's course and speed (090°, 20kts) plotted. A tangent to the arc of the submarine's speed is drawn from the 20nm mark, giving the relative course the submarine must make good at 16 knots to successfully attack.

which a submarine threat might come. The outer zone will normally be patrolled by long-range maritime patrol aircraft (LRMP), using a variety of sensors, including radar, sonobuoys, and magnetic anomaly detectors (MAD). Most such LRMP aircraft also carry weapons to attack targets they have detected.

Next is a zone patrolled by ships, aircraft and friendly submarines. The ships would mostly deploy passive towed arrays such as the US Navy's Tactical Towed Acoustic Sensor System (TACTASS). This is also the area in which SSNs would patrol, covering large areas of sea, alternating bursts of speed with periods of virtual immobility as they "listen" with their passive sonars for any trace of enemy surface or submarine activity.

In the inner zone is the Task Group itself, following a zig-zag course, a tactic which acts as a final deterrent to submarine attack, but which restricts its overall speed of advance to about 10 knots (18.5km/h). In this inner zone will be the active sonar ships, each operating within a closely coordinated plan, and manoeuvring continuously to prevent submarines setting up a firing solution for their weapons. This is also the zone where the ASW helicopters operate, using their third dimension – agility – to cover vast areas of ocean and to move into new areas without any warning to any submarines lurking below.

Left: The ASW systems station in a Royal Navy SeaKing helicopter. Helicopters have played a large part in restoring the balance between surface warships and submarines, and are extremely effective ASW platforms, especially as they are very difficult for submarines to detect.

7

Carrier Directory

VEINTICINCO DE MAYO
(British Colossus) class (Argentina)

Origin: UK
Ships in Class: *Veinticinco de Mayo*
Displacement: 15,892 tons (16,146 tonnes) standard; 19,896 tons (20,214 tonnes) full load
Dimensions: Length 697ft 8in (212.79m); Beam — Hull 80ft 4in (24.50m); Flight Deck 133ft 4in (40.66m); Draught 24ft 6in (7.47m)
Armament: 9 x 40mm AA guns
Propulsion: Geared turbines, 40,000shp; 2 propellers
Performance: Speed 24 knots; range 6,200nm (11,490km) at 23 knots
Complement: 1,509 Officers and Ratings (total)
Air Wing: 4 McDonnell-Douglas A-4Q Skyhawk; 5 Grumman S-2E Tracker; 3 (or 4) Sikorsky SH-3D/H Sea King; 1 (or 2) Aerospatiale Alouette III

Background: This elderly ship was laid down on 3 December 1942 as HMS *Venerable*, one of the Colossus class of ''light fleet carriers'', a particularly successful British design. She served in the Royal Navy's Pacific Fleet at the end of the Second World War and on her return was sold to the Netherlands, who commissioned her in 1948 as the *Karel Doorman*, primarily for service in the Dutch East Indies. She underwent a major reconstruction between 1955 and 1958, being fitted with an 8 deg-angled flight-deck, mirror landing gear, steam catapults and new radar.

In 1967 she suffered fire damage and was rebuilt and fitted with new boilers, taken from an incomplete British carrier. She was then sold to Argentina in 1968, was refitted yet again, then commissioned into the Argentine Navy in 1969. The flight-deck was enlarged in 1980 and altered again in 1982 to prepare her for operating Super Etendard aircraft, which had been bought from France. However, sea trials eventually convinced all concerned that the ship just could not operate these aircraft, despite the undoubted skill of the Argentine Navy pilots, and the Super Etendards have since flown only from shore bases.

In the Falklands War of 1982, the Argentine Navy Battle Group which was centred upon the *Veinticinco de Mayo* was a very serious threat to the British Task Force. At one stage in the campaign the Battle Group was at sea ready to attack, but the weather was too bad to launch and recover the Air Group, and attack had to be abandoned.

The carrier has been inactive since 1986 due to engineering problems. However, with Argentina's financial difficulties there is no question of purchasing a new carrier and so the Argentine Navy will doubtless continue its efforts to re-engine the *Veinticinco de Mayo* and get her back to sea again.

Below: The Argentine carrier *Veinticinco de Mayo* was built as the British *Venerable.* She was bought by the Dutch in 1948 and renamed *Karel Doorman*. She was then sold to Argentina in 1969. She was unable to take a major operational role in the Falklands War in 1982.

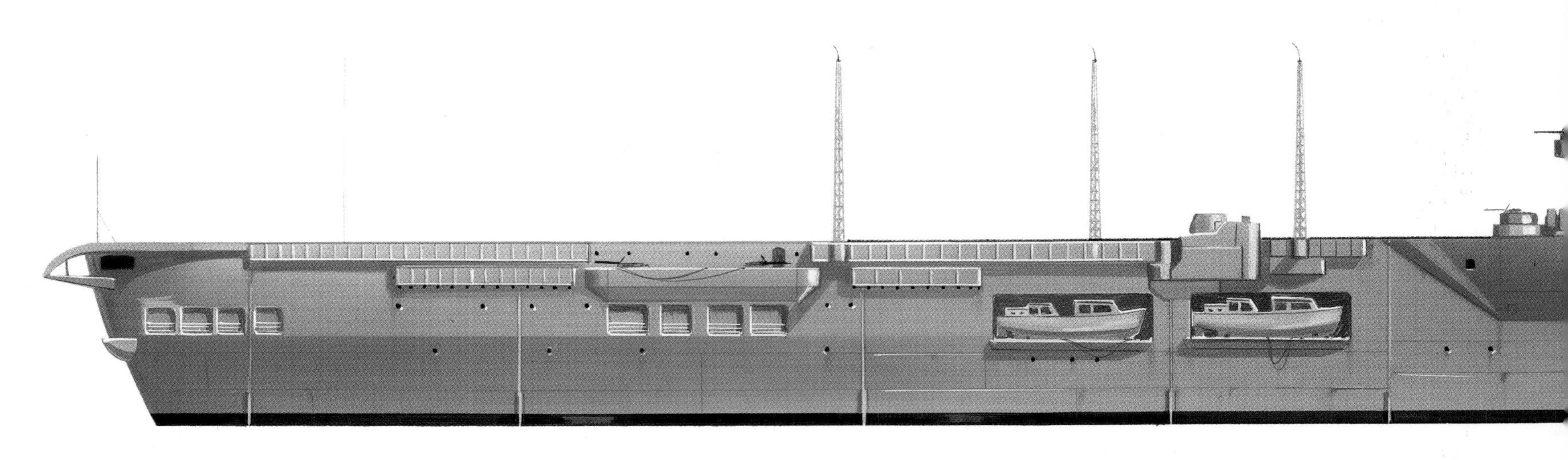

MINAS GERAIS (British Colossus) class (Brazil)

Origin: UK
Ships in Class: *Minas Gerais* (A-11)
Displacement: 15,890 tons (16,144 tonnes) standard; 19,890 tons (20,208 tonnes) full load
Dimensions: Length 693ft 1in (211.38m); Beam — Hull 80ft 4in (24.50m); Flight Deck 119ft 6in (36.45m); Draught 23ft 5in (7.14m)
Armament: 10 × 40mm AA guns
Propulsion: Geared turbines, 42,000shp; 2 propellers
Performance: Speed 24 knots; range 12,000nm (22,238km) at 14 knots
Complement: 1,000 Ship's Company, 300 Air Wing
Air Wing: 6 (or 8) Grumman S-2E Tracker; 4 (or 6) Sikorsky SH-3 Sea King; 2 Bell SAH-11 (208B JetRanger); 3 Aerospatiale UH-12 (AS.350 Eqsquilo)

Background: The Brazilian Navy carrier *Minas Gerais* is a sister ship to the Argentine Navy's *Veinticinco de Mayo*, both having been originally built as units of the wartime British Colossus class. Originally commissioned as HMS *Vengeance*, she served in the Royal Navy from 1945 until 1965, when she was sold to Brazil. She was subsequently sent by Brazil to Rotterdam for a three-year refit, where she was fitted with an 8.5 deg-angled flight deck, mirror landing gear and two new deck elevators.

Throughout her career in the Brazilian Navy she has been employed as an ASW carrier, operating a mix of helicopters and fixed-wing Grumman S-2E Trackers, the latter being flown by Air Force crews. There was a proposal in the early-1980s to purchase twelve A-4 Skyhawk aircraft, but this was later dropped.

In 1987 problems with her catapults led to her being taken out of service pending a refit, which still had not been started in 1991. It is thus questionable whether the *Minas Gerais* will return to service, although possibility remains, particularly if the Argentine Navy – the Brazilian Navy's great rival – was to succeed in refitting its own carrier.

Above: The only other carrier in a Latin American navy, Brazil's *Minas Gerais* was also built as a unit of the British Colossus class. Used by the Brazilians as an ASW carrier, she has been out of service since 1987.

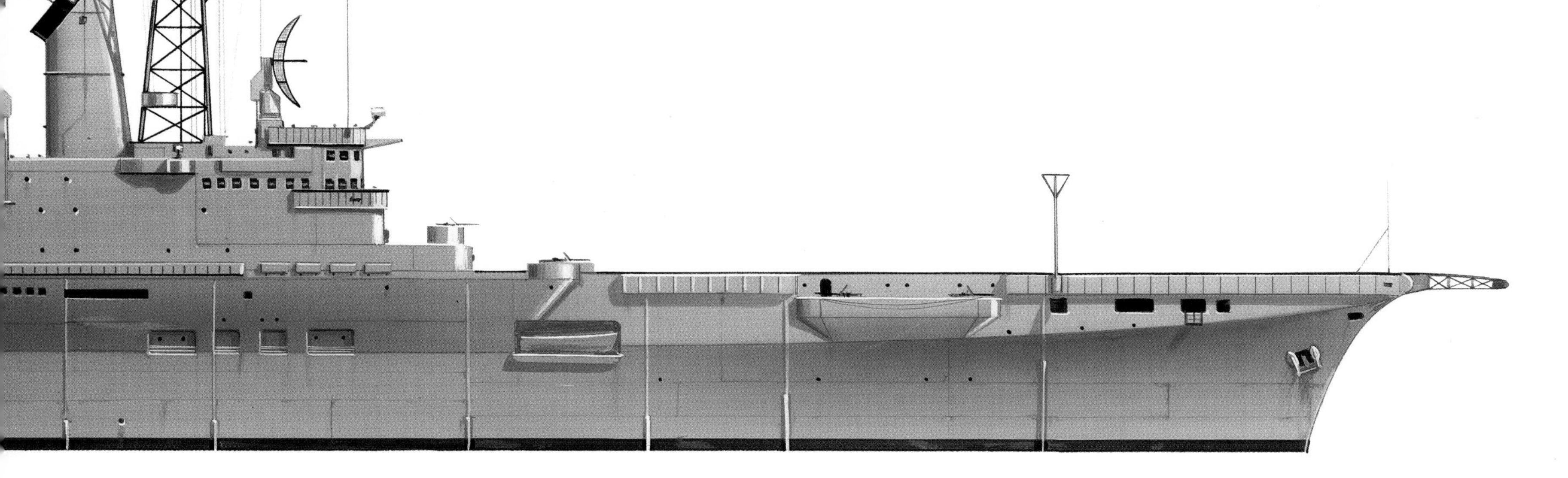

CHARLES DE GAULLE class (France)

Origin: France
Ships in Class: *Charles de Gaulle* (R-91); (unnamed)
Displacement: 33,500 tons (34,036 tonnes) standard; 36,000 tons (36,576 tonnes) full load
Dimensions: Length 857ft 9in (261.61m); Beam — Hull 103ft 3in (31.49m); Flight Deck 211ft 2in (64.40m); Draught 27ft 9in (8.46m)
Armament: 32 × SAAM vertical launch SAM; SADRAL point defence SAM; 8 × 20mm AA
Propulsion: Nuclear, 83,000shp; 2 propellers
Performance: Speed 27 knots
Complement: 1,150 Ships's Company, 550 Air Wing
Air Wing: 35-40 aircraft (see text)

Background: The French have undertaken a number of very ambitious naval programmes over the past forty years, but none in such a high-risk area as these two nuclear-propelled aircraft carriers. Intended to replace *Clemenceau* and *Foch*, the first, *Charles de Gaulle*, will join the French Navy in 1998 and the second (as yet unnamed) in 2002. The hull design is based upon that of the Clemenceau class, with very similar dimensions, but obviously with major developments to reflect the latest advances in carrier practice, including a substantial missile armament. In a very unusual step the French have built a 20-ton (20.32 tonne) scale model of the new carrier, which is being used for hydrodynamic development and systems integration. This unique vessel has a crew of three.

Provision of the Air Wings will be a very expensive undertaking. Initially the Super Etendard will be operated, but it is planned that this will eventually be replaced by the Rafale M strike aircraft, although it remains a possibility that the US F/A-18 Hornet may be purchased. An AEW aircraft is absolutely essential, but no order has yet been placed. One possibility is that Grumman E-2C Hawkeyes will be bought, although an alternative could be rebuilt Grumman S-2E Trackers, which would have a new French radar and turboprop engines.

The K15 nuclear-propulsion plant is the latest in a series of very successful French designs, which includes the smallest operational marine reactor in the world, which is installed in the Rubis and Amethyste class submarines. This will give the carriers virtually unlimited range. These two nuclear-propelled carriers will give the French what is unquestionably the most powerful surface warfare capability of any European navy in the early years of the 21st Century.

CLEMENCEAU class (France)

Origin: France
Ships in Class: *Clemenceau* (R-98); *Foch* (R-99)
Displacement: 24,200 tons (24,587 tonnes) standard; 32,700 tons (33,223 tonnes) full load
Dimensions: Length 869ft 4in (265.14m); Beam — Hull 104ft 1in (31.74m); Flight Deck 168ft (51.24m); Draught 28ft 2in (8.59m)
Armament: 2 × Crotale SAM systems; 4 × 100mm DP Guns
Propulsion: Geared turbines, 126,000shp; 2 propellers
Performance: Speed 32 knots; range 4,800nm (8,895km) at 23 knots
Complement: 1,338 Ship's Company, 582 Air Wing
Air Wing: 16 Dassault Super Etendard; 10 LTV F-8E (FN) Crusader; 3 Dassault Etendard IVP; 7 Breguet Alize; 2 + Aerospatiale SA-365N Dauphin helicopters

Background: In the early post-war years the French Navy operated five aircraft car-

Above: The first French carrier to be built after World War II *Clemenceau* has been in service since 1961. She is due to be replaced by the first of the new nuclear-propelled carriers, *Charles de Gaulle*, in 1998.

Below: Weapons include: (A) 2x1 100mm DP gun; (B) 2x1 100mm DP gun; (C) 2x1 100mm DP gun; (D) 2x1 100mm DP gun; (E) 2x1 100mm DP gun. Her electronics suite includes: (1) SQS-505 hull-mounted sonar; (2) DRBC-32A gunfire control radar; (3) DRBN-32 navigation radar; (4) DRBI-10C height-finding radar; (5) DRBV-23B air search radar; (6) DRBV-50 surface radar; (7) SRN-6 Tacan; (8) DRBV-20C long-range radar; (9) DRBI-10C height-finding radar; (10) approach radar.

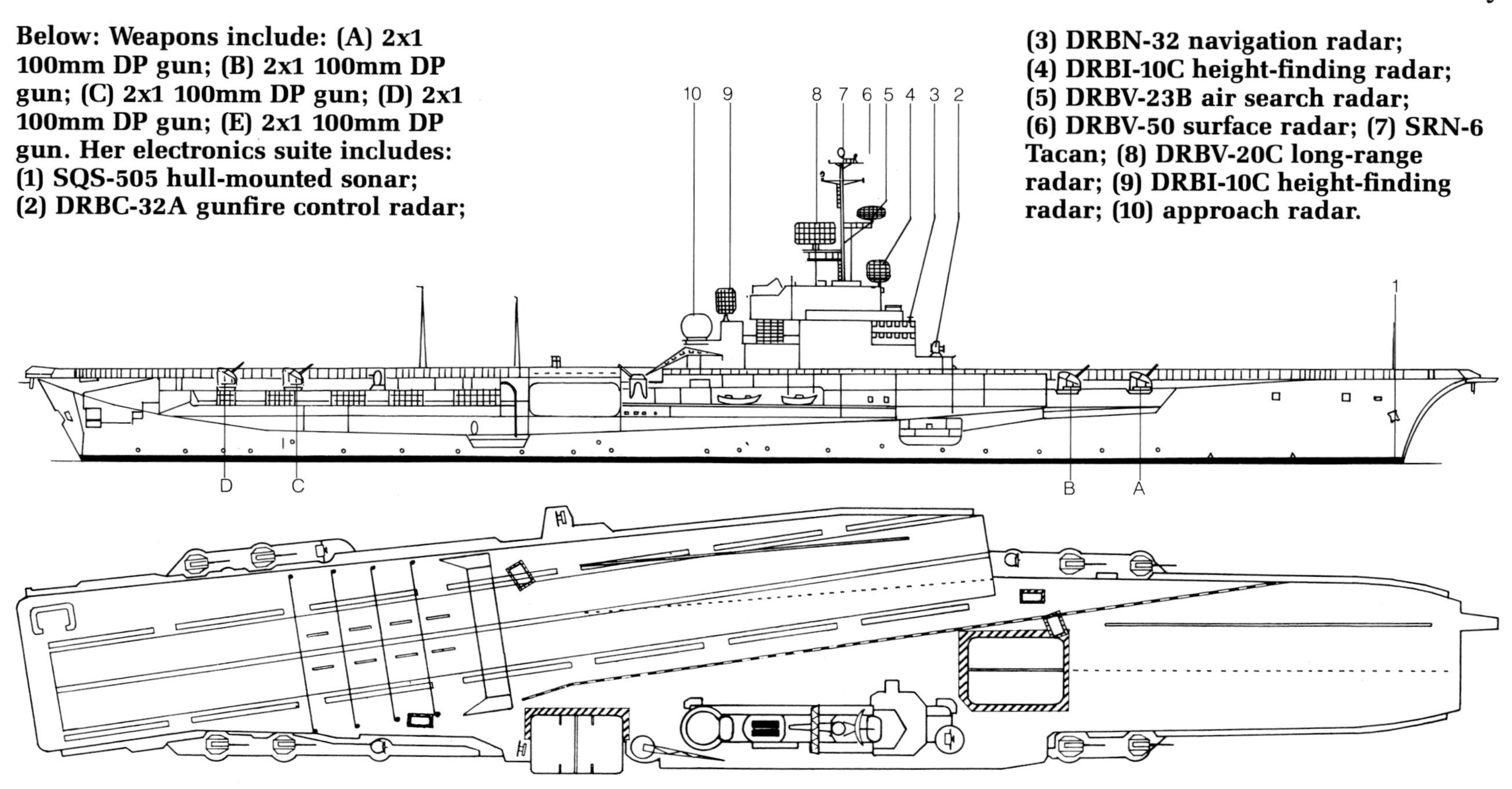

riers. The oldest was the pre-war French carrier, *Bearn*, which was of limited value. Two were lent by the USA in 1946, *Bois Belleau* and *La Fayette*, being returned in 1960 and 1963 respectively. The third, *Dixmude*, a converted cargo ship, was transferred from Great Britain's Royal Navy in 1945, but was used mainly as an aircraft transport. The best was the *Arromanches*, formerly HMS *Colossus*, the name ship of her class of "light fleet carriers", which was lent by the Royal Navy in 1946 and eventually purchased outright by the French Government in 1951.

The French Navy replaced these with a class of two carriers of indigenous design, both of which were laid down in the 1950s, incorporting all the advances in carrier practice made in the early post-war period. They have served the French Navy well, operating in the Pacific in support of the remaining French colonial territories and of the nuclear test programme, as well as supporting operations closer to home; for example, off Lebanon and in the Gulf War.

They are of conventional design, with an 8 deg-angled deck. The French developed a series of aircraft specifically for service on these ships, including Etendard and Super Etendard strike fighters and the Alize ASW aircraft. However, the selected fighter was the US Navy's F-8E Crusader, 42 of which were delivered in the late-1960s and which have given the French many years of excellent service.

Both ships have received several major refits during their service, but are now reaching the end of their useful lives and are due to be paid off when they are replaced by the two new nuclear carriers: *Clemenceau* is planned to go in 1998 and *Foch* in 2002.

Above: *Foch* was used for some years as an ASW carrier, but in 1987-88 refit she was brought up to the same standard as *Clemenceau*. She will be replaced by the second, as yet unnamed, nuclear carrier in 2002.

ENTERPRISE class (USA)

Origin: USA
Ships in Class: *Enterprise* (CVN-65)
Displacement: 74,730 tons (75,926 tonnes) standard; 92,200 tons (93,675 tonnes) full load
Dimensions: Length 1,108ft 3in (338m); Beam — Hull 132ft 9in (40.49m); Flight Deck 257ft 2in (78.44m); Draught 39ft 0in (11.89m)
Armament: 2 x Mk 29 launchers for Sea Sparrow SAM; 3 x Mk 15 20mm CIWS
Propulsion: Nuclear, 280,000shp; 4 propellers
Performance: Speed 33 knots
Complement: 2,937 Ship's Company, 2,627 Air Wing
Air Wing: 24 Grumman F-14A Tomcat; 24 McDonnell-Douglas F/A-18A Hornet; 10 Grumman A-6E Intruder; 4 Grumman KA-6D Intruder; 4 Grumman EA-6B Prowler; 4 Grumman E-2C Hawkeye; 10 Lockheed S-3A Viking; 6 Sikorsky SH-3H Sea King

Above: USS *Enterprise* was the first nuclear-propelled aircraft carrier, being powered by eight A2W reactors, each producing 35,000shp. Many of her air group of eighty aircraft are seen here on her massive flight-deck.

Background: The US Navy's first nuclear-powered surface warship was the cruiser USS *Long Beach* (CGN-9), and the first nuclear-propelled carrier, USS *Enterprise* (CGN-65), was laid down shortly afterwards, being launched just 31 months later and commissioned just fourteen months after that — a remarkable achievement.

Because the Westinghouse A2W nuclear reactors had the comparatively low power output of 35,000shp, no less than eight had to be installed to give the required performance. The overall cost was $451.3million, an astronomical sum at that time; it was estimated to be twice that of an oil-fuelled aircraft carrier of the same displacement and capability, and actually led to the cancellation of five other ships. Nevertheless, virtually limitless range and increased aviation fuel capacity made USS *Enterprise* relatively cheap to run; indeed, she can sustain no less than twelve days of intensive air operations before she needs to replenish from a tanker and even has bunkers for fuel-oil to replenish conventionally-powered ships in the Task Force.

USS *Enterprise* is similar in layout and general size to the Kitty Hawk class, but her island structure is significantly different as there is no need for exhaust stacks. Prior to her first refit she had four large planar arrays on a box structure for her main radar, but this was replaced by the more usual rotating arrays in 1979.

USS *Enterprise* operated for many years with the Pacific Fleet, but now serves in the Atlantic. Her present life expectancy is to the year 2011.

FORRESTAL class (USA)

Origin: USA
Ships in Class: *Forrestal* (CV-59); *Saratoga* (CV-60); *Ranger* (CV-61); *Independence* (CV-62)
Displacement: 60,000 tons (60,960 tonnes) light; 79,250 to 80,643 tons (80,518 to 81,933 tonnes) full load
Dimensions: Length 1,086ft (331.23m) (see notes); Beam — Hull 129ft 9in (39.57m); Flight Deck 250ft 3in (76.32m); Draught 37ft 1in (11.31m)
Armament: 2 x Mk 29 launchers for Sea Sparrow SAM; 3 x 20mm Mk 15 CIWS
Propulsion: Geared turbines, 280,000shp; 4 propellers
Performance: Speed 33 knots; range 4,000nm (7,412km) at 30 knots
Complement: 2,790 Ship's Company, 3,390 Air Wing
Air Wing: 20 Grumman F-14A Tomcat; 24 McDonnell-Douglas F/A-18A Hornet; 10 Grumman A-6E Intruder; 4 Grumman KA-6D Intruder; 4 Grumman EA-6B Prowler; 4 Grumman E-2C Hawkeye; 10 Lockheed S-3A Viking; 6 Sikorsky SH-3H Sea King

Right: USS *Forrestal*, the first of the super carriers, entered service in 1955. The angled flight-deck was tested on the *Antietam* and later incorporated into the *Forrestal*.

Background: USS *Forrestal* (CV-59), launched on 11 December 1954, established an impressive list of "firsts". She was the first aircraft carrier in the world to be built after the Second World War, the first designed specifically to operate turbojet aircraft and the first to operate nuclear bombers, namely North American A-3 Skywarriors. She was also the first US carrier to have an armoured flight-deck, an enclosed bow and steam catapults. She was originally designed with a straight-through flight-deck, but following successful tests of the angled deck on USS *Antietam* (CV-36) in 1952, an 8 deg-angled deck was installed during construction.

There are minor differences between the four ships in length, displacement, armament and Air Wings, of which the most curious is that USS *Forrestal* has three rudders and four propellers, the inboard pair having four blades and the outboard pair five. Three of the carriers have received the major Service Life Extension Program (SLEP) improvements, but the fourth, USS *Ranger* (CV-61) has received only a major refit.

USS *Ranger* is due to decommission in 1999 and the other three will follow in the first decade of the 21st Century. Despite their many innovations and many years of distinguished front-line service, the Forrestal class suffer a number of limitations, perhaps the most important of which is that launching and landing aircraft simultaneously is difficult.

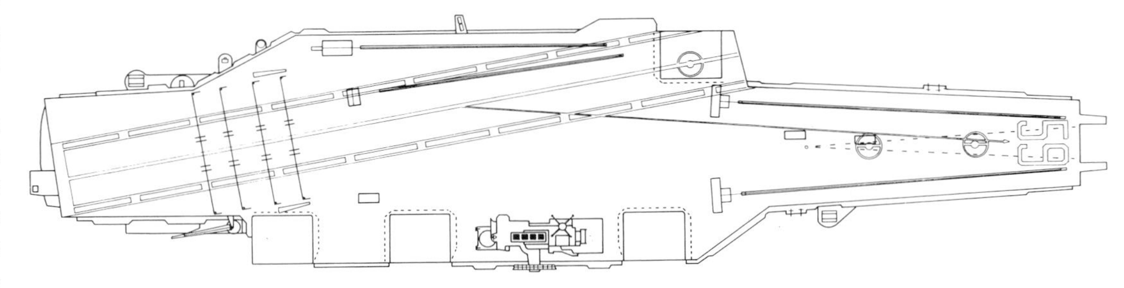

Right Centre: *Forrestal's* deck-plan shows how the angled deck left the foredeck clear for launching, but the elevator at the forward end of the angled deck proved to be inconvenient. Two steam catapults were fitted.

Right: USS *Saratoga*, second ship of the Forrestal class at sea, with 47 aircraft of her eighty-strong air wing on deck. With *Forrestal* she has operated in the Atlantic Fleet since commissioning in April 1956.

GIUSEPPE GARIBALDI class (Italy)

Origin: Italy
Ships in Class: *Giuseppe Garibaldi* (C-551); *Giuseppe Mazzini* (planned)
Displacement: 9,360 tons (9,510 tonnes) standard; 13,240 tons (13,452 tonnes) full load
Dimensions: Length 591ft 2in (180.30m); Beam — Hull 78ft 1in (23.81m); Flight Deck 99ft 7in (30.37m); Draught 22ft (6.71m)
Armament: 4 × Otomat-Teseo Mk 2 SSM; 2 × Albatross SAM; 6 × 40mm AA; 6 × 324mm torpedo tubes
Propulsion: Gas turbines, 80,000shp; 2 propellers
Performance: Speed 29.5 knots; range 7,000nm (12,972km) at 20 knots
Complement: 560 total
Air Wing: 16 Agusta/Sikorsky SH-3D Sea King

Background: The Italian Navy sought to construct two aircraft carriers during the second World War, both being conversions from passenger liners, but neither was completed. During the Cold War, the Italian Navy built some excellent cruisers and destroyers fitted with large flight decks which could operate quite large numbers of helicopters. The cruiser *Vittorio Veneto*, for example, has a flight deck 131ft (39.95m) long and 61ft (18.60m) wide and operates six Agusta-Bell AB.212 ASW helicopters.

It was not until 1978, however, that political agreement was obtained to construct a ship with a full-length flight-deck; although, as with the British "through-deck cruisers", the design purported to be a cruiser with an increased air capability, rather than a "proper" aircraft carrier. An additional problem was that under a long-standing law the Italian Air Force was responsible for the provision of fixed-wing aircraft for the Italian Navy, and the modern Air Force declined flatly either to operate Sea Harriers for the Navy or to allow the Navy to operate such aircraft on its own account. This impasse lasted well beyond the entry into service of the *Giuseppe Garibaldi* and has only recently been resolved by amending the law to allow the Navy to operate its own aircraft. It is of interest that, despite this squabble, a small 6deg "ski-jump" was built into the original design, although it was tartly announced by the Navy that this was intended only to ensure the "dryness" of the forward part of the flight-deck in heavy sea conditions!

The *Giuseppe Garibaldi* is an except-

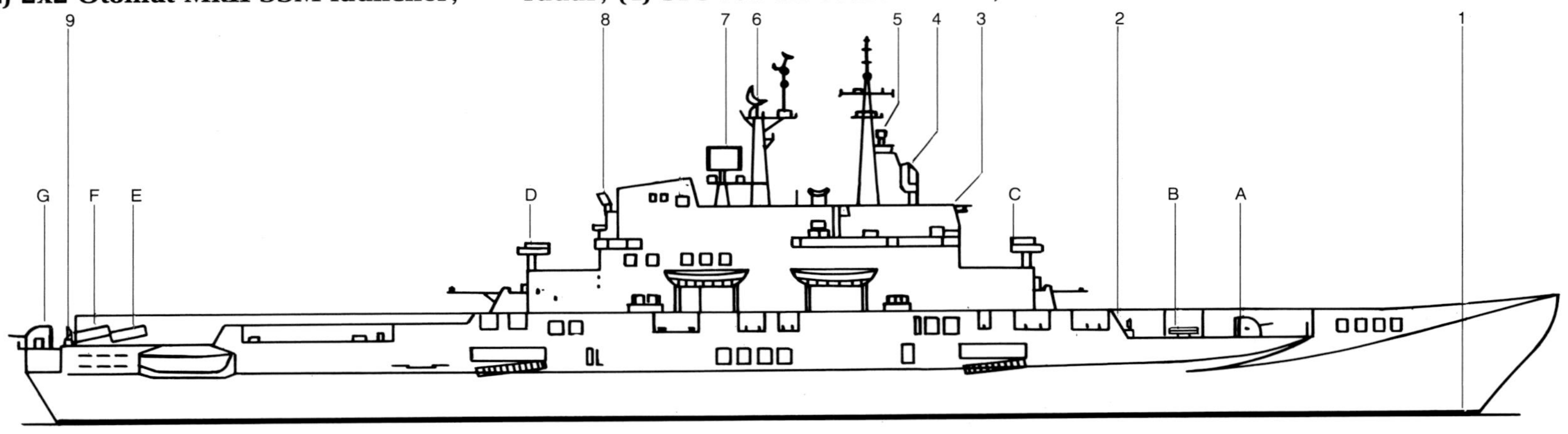

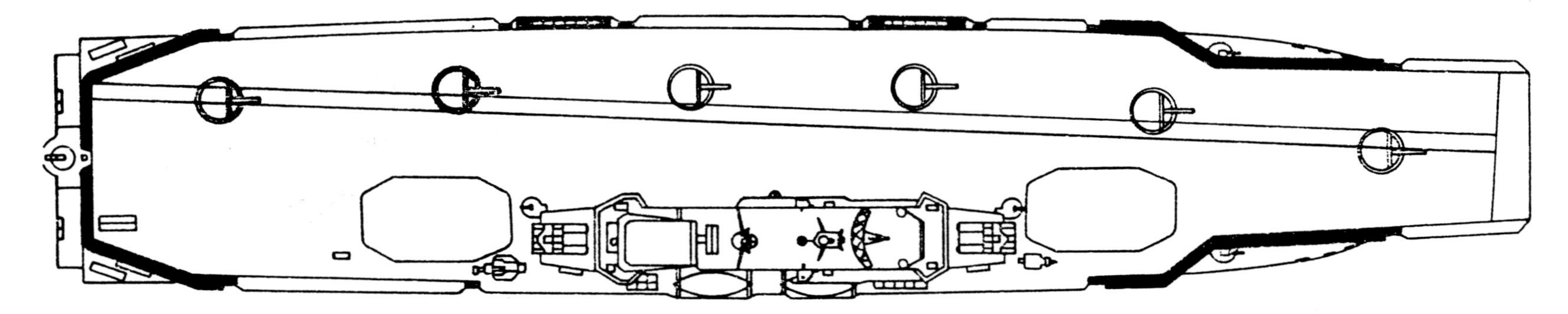

Below: Weapons on Garibaldi include: (A) 2x2 40mm Dardo CIWS; (B) 2x3 Mk 32 ASW torpedo tubes; (C) 1x8 Aspide SAM launcher; (D) 1x8 Aspide SAM launcher; (E) 2x2 Otomat MkII SSM launcher; (F) 2x2 Otomat Mk II SSM launcher; (G) 1x2 40mm Dardo CIWS. Electronics include: (1) DE-1164F hull-mounted sonar; (2) RTN-20X radar for Dardo CIWS; (3) SPN-703 navigation radar; (4) SPS-768 air search radar; (5) SPS-702 surface radar; (6) SPS-774 short range air defence radar; (7) RTN-30X radar for Aspide fire control; (8) RTN-20X radar for Dardo CIWS; (9) RTN-20X for Dardo CIWS. Two deck elevators can also be seen.

Above: a fine stern view of *Giuseppe Garibaldi* at the time she was conducting trials with RN Sea Harriers, four of which can be seen on her flight-deck. There was a long inter-service fight between the Italian Navy and Air Force over the provision of fixed-wing aircraft, the latter quoting a 1929 law passed by Mussolini to justify their stand!

Right: A US Marine Corps AV-8B Harrier II on *Giuseppe Garibaldi's* ski-jump during a later set of trials. Having settled the dispute with the Air Force, the Italian Navy has selected the AV-8B in preference to the Sea Harrier and these will be flown by naval pilots. This ship also has a heavy defensive armament installed.

tionally neat design with an unangled flight deck and two lifts. Her intended role is as an ASW carrier, for which she can carry up to 16 Sea Kings, although the normal complement is 12. A slightly smaller number of the new EH-101 helicopters will be carried when the latter type enters service.

Extensive flight trials have been carried out with Royal Navy Sea Harriers and an order for McDonnell-Douglas AV-8B Harrier IIs has subsequently been placed. A maximum of ten AV-8Bs will be operated, or a lesser number in combination with helicopters.

The Italians have a firm commitment to disaster relief work and a capability for such operations has been designed into this ship. She has a heavy armament for her size and role, consisting of four SSM launchers, two SAM launchers and six AA guns, together with — and most unusually for a Western aircraft carrier — six torpedo tubes.

A second ship is planned by the Italian Navy, which may displace some 1,000 tons (1,016 tonnes) more than the *Giuseppe Garibaldi*. This ship will most probably be named *Giuseppe Mazzini*, although the name *Conte di Cavour* has also been mentioned. If the Italian Navy gets its way then a third ship could also be ordered.

INVINCIBLE class (UK)

Origin: UK
Ships in Class: *Invincible* (R-05); *Illustrious* (R-06); *Ark Royal* (R-07)
Displacement: 16,860 tons (17,130 tonnes) standard; 20,600 tons (20,930 tonnes) full load
Dimensions: Length 689ft (210.14m); Beam — Hull 104ft 7in (31.90m); Flight Deck 90ft 2in (27.50m); Draught 21ft 3in (6.48m)
Armament: 1 x Sea Dart GWS.30 SAM; *Invincible* — 3 x 30mm Goalkeeper CIWS; *Illustrious* — 2 x 20mm Mk15 CIWS; *Ark Royal* — 3 x 20mm Mk 15 CIWS; all — 2 x 20mm GAM-BO1 AA
Propulsion: Gas turbines, 112,000shp; 2 propellers
Performance: Speed 28 knots; range 7,000nm (12,972km) at 18 knots
Complement: *Invincible* — 666 Ship's Company, 402 Air Wing; *Illustrious, Ark Royal* — 1,000 Ship's Company, 318 Air Wing
Air Wing: 9 BAe Sea Harrier FRS.1; 3 Westland Sea King AEW.2; 9 Sea King Mk 5 ASW

Background: The Royal Navy invented the aircraft carrier and most of its major equipment advances, such as the angled-deck, armoured flight-decks, mirror landing aids, steam catapults and the "ski-jump". Furthermore, until recently the Royal Navy operated the second largest carrier fleet in the world; in 1960, for example, there were five large carriers (HMS *Ark Royal, Eagle, Victorious, Hermes* and *Centaur*), and two commando carriers (*Albion* and *Bulwark*) in service. Today, the Royal Navy possesses just three light aircraft carriers, of which only two are actually in service at any one time.

Without the air cover provided by HMS *Invincible* and the older HMS *Hermes*, the British Task Force sent to recapture the Falkland Islands in 1982 could never have succeeded. In fact, the British were rather lucky to have even these ships, especially HMS *Invincible*, which had had a very checkered career and has been on the verge of cancellation for financial reasons on several occasions.

Initially, these ships were described as 'through-deck cruisers" and were intended to operate an Air Wing composed only of ASW helicopters. Then, rather late in the design process, provision had to be made to operate Sea Harrier fighter aircraft to intercept hostile reconnaissance and ASW patrol aircraft. Finally, in 1976-77 it was decided to incorporate facilities for these vessels to act as commando carriers, as well.

The flight-deck is angled very slightly to port to avoid the Sea Dart launcher on the forecastle. HMS *Invincible* and HMS *Illustrious* were constructed with a 7deg "ski-jump", while HMS *Ark Royal* was the first to have the full 12deg device, which is also some 39ft (11.89m) longer, thus enabling the full-load carrying capability of the Sea Harrier to be exploited. All three can carry a Royal Marine commando group (906 men) for short, if somewhat crowded, periods.

The hangar is a "dumb-bell" shape, the narrow centre being needed to accommodate the gas-turbine exhausts. This obviously limits the movements of the Sea Harriers below, although the problem has been eased somewhat during subsequent major refits.

The three carriers entered service between 1980 and 1985. In 1986 the first, HMS *Invincible* entered a three-year refit, which included improved hangar facilities, a 12deg "ski-jump", and larger magazine able to accommodate the new Sea Eagle missile and Stingray ASW torpedoes. In addition, the Mk 15 Phalanx CIWS, which had been fitted in haste during the Falklands War, was replaced by three Dutch Goalkeeper systems. All three ships are fitted with extensive flag-ship facilities enabling them to take command of Tasks Groups.

The Royal Navy intends to keep two of the three ships in commission at any one time, the third being either laid-up or in refit prior to returning to service.

Left: HMS *Illustrious* in 1983. The second of her class, she had just been hastily fitted with two Vulcan/Phalanx CIWS; one can be seen on the foredeck, the other at the stern.

Above: HMS *Invincible* refuelling from the replenishment ship RFA *Olmeda.* The twin-arm Sea Dart SAM launcher can be clearly seen on the foredeck. The 7° 'ski-jump' on *Invincible* and *Illustrious*, as seen here, has been replaced by a full 12° device, in *Ark Royal*.

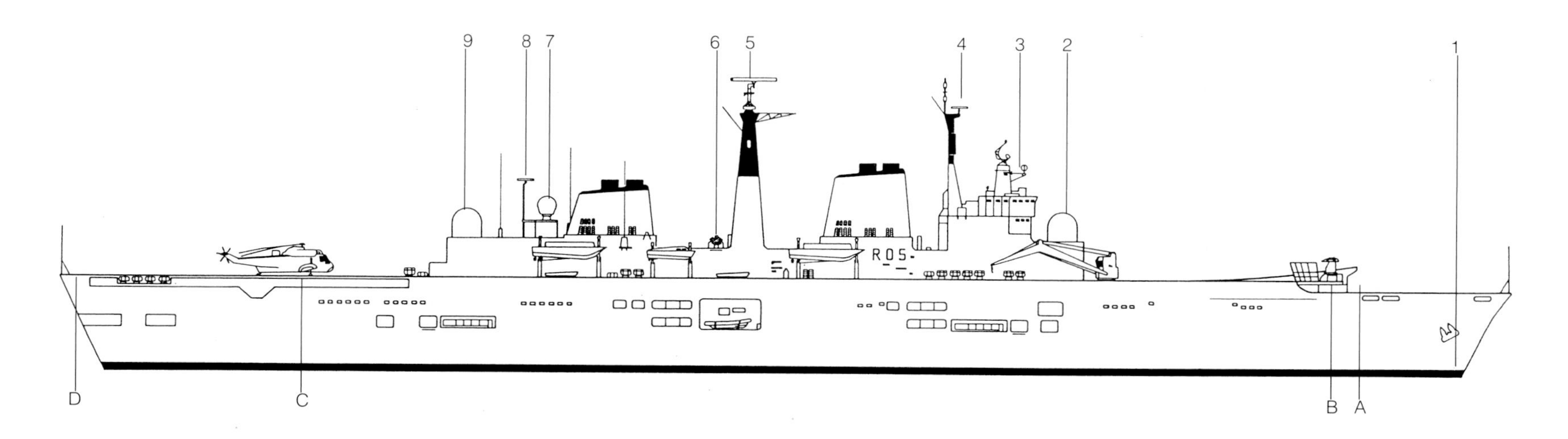

Below: This view shows one of the first two ships with the 7° ski jump. Weapons include: (A) 1x1 Mk 15 Phalanx CIWS; (B) 1x2 Sea Dart SAM launcher; (C) Sea King Helicopter; (D) 1x1 Mk 15 Phalanx CIWS. Electronics fit includes: (1) Type 2016 hull-mounted sonar; (2) Type 909 fire-control radar; (3) Type 1022 long-range radar; (4) Type 1006 navigation radar; (5) Type 922R search radar; (6) 2x8 Corvus chaff launcher; (7) 2x1 SCOT satellite terminal; (8) Type 1006 navigation radar; (9) Type 909 fire-control radar. These ships are the first of the new type of V/STOL carriers.

Origin: USA
Ships in Class: *Iwo Jima* (LPH-2); *Okinawa* (LPH-3); *Guadalcanal* (LPH-7); *Guam* (LPH-9); *Tripoli* (LPH-10); *New Orleans* (LPH-11); *Inchon* (LPH-12)
Displacement: 11,000 tons (11,176 tonnes) standard; 18,300 tons (18,593 tonnes) full load
Dimensions: Length 602ft 4in (183.71m); Beam — Hull 83ft 7in (25.49m); Flight Deck 104ft (31.72m); Draught 25ft 9in (7.85m)
Armament: 4×76.2mm DP; 2×Mk 25 launchers for Sea Sparrow SAM; 2×20mm Mk 15 CIWS (not in LPH-3); 4, 6 or 8×12.7mm MG
Propulsion: Geared turbines, 23,000shp; 1 propeller
Performance: Speed 23 knots
Complement: 685 Ship's Company, 2,090 Troops
Air Wing: 20-24 Boeing-Vertol CH-46 Sea Knight; 4 Sikorsky CH-53 Sea Stallion; 4 Bell UH-1 Iroquois/AH-1 Sea Cobra

Background: Experiments with the use of helicopters for "vertical assault" started in the late-1940s, and in 1955 the US Navy converted the escort carrier USS *Thetis Bay* (CVE-90) into a helicopter assault ship, it being redesignated LPH-1. The success of the concept led to the design of a class of purpose-built ships, the first of which, USS *Iwo Jima* (LPH-2) entered service in 1961.

These ships were not considered to require full fleet performance and so a merchant-ship hull design was selected with a single propeller. They have a large, unangled flight-deck, with two folding, deck-edge lifts giving access to the hangar, which can accommodate up to 19 CH-46 or 11 CH-53 transport helicopters.

Some 2,000 Marines can be carried, accommodated in living-spaces fore and aft of the hangar.

In addition to their amphibious warfare role these ships can also act as carriers for RH-53/MH-53E minesweeping helicopters or AV-8B Harrier fighters. USS *Guam* (LPH-9), was used for the trials of the Sea Control Ship (SCS) concept in the early-1970s, operating a mix of AV-8A Harriers and ASW helicopters. Although the trials themselves were successful, the overall concept was not at that time popular in the US Navy and was eventually dropped, USS *Guam* reverting to her amphibious warfare role.

These ships have proved their worth repeatedly over the past thirty years and have taken part in numerous operations in the Far East, Middle East and Central

Above: USS *Tripoli*, a Guam class assault ship, which can operate as a carrier for marines with CH-46 helicopters, for minesweeping missions with MH-53E helicopters, or for strike missions with AV-8B Harriers.

America. Their major limitations have been the lack of a docking-well, thus necessitating helicopters for ship-to-shore movements, and the use of only a single propeller, which unfortunately limits speed and manoeuvrability. The Iwo-Jimas are due to be replaced by the Wasp class during the 1990s.

Right: USS *Guadalcanal* in the Gulf with a variety of helicopter types on her flight-deck including: CH-53 Sea Stallions, CH-46 Sea Knights, UH-1 Iroquois and AH-1 Sea Cobras. The class has proved very successful.

JEANNE D'ARC class (France)

Origin: France
Ships in Class: *Jeanne d'Arc* (R-97)
Displacement: 10,575 tons (10,744 tonnes) standard; 13,270 tons (13,482 tonnes) full load
Dimensions: Length 597ft (182.08m); Beam — Hull 72ft 2in (22.01m); Flight Deck 78ft 7in (23.97m); Draught 23ft 9in (7.24m)
Armament: 6 × MM-38 Exocet SSM; 4 × 100mm Model 1953 guns; 4 × 12.7mm MG
Propulsion: Geared turbines, 40,000shp; 2 propellers
Performance: Speed 26.5 knots; range 5,500nm (10,192km) at 20 knots
Complement: 627 Ship's Company
Air Wing: 3 Aerospatiale Lynx; 3 Aerospatiale Alouette III (see notes)

Background: *Jeanne d'Arc* is an interesting design, which is employed in peacetime as a cadet training ship, but which in time of war would be used as an ASW helicopter carrier or as an amphibious transport. The normal complement of helicopters in peacetime is shown above, but in war simple structural changes, in particular removing the midshipmen's accommodation, would enable the much larger Super Frelon ASW helicopters to be carried on board.

The hull design was based on that of the air defence cruiser *Colbert*, but the aft part of the superstructure is devoted to a large flight-deck 203ft (62m) in length and 69ft (21m) wide. There is a single centre-line lift at the aft end of the flight-deck.

Jeanne d'Arc has a significant surface armament, with six Exocet launchers and four 100mm guns. However, the ship's air defence armament is negligible and in war she would have to depend entirely on other ships in the Battle Group for her protection.

Above: *Jeanne d'Arc*, with an RAF Harrier on the flight-deck, during trials. A very useful ship, she is used for training in peacetime, but in war she would be used as an ASW carrier or amphibious transport.

KIEV class (USSR)

Origin: USSR
Ships in Class: *Kiev*; *Minsk*; *Novorossiysk*
Displacement: 36,000 tons (36,576 tonnes) standard; 43,000 tons (43,688 tonnes) full load
Dimensions: Length 895ft 7in (273.15m); Beam — Hull 107ft 3in (32.71m); Flight Deck 173ft 9in (53m); Draught 31ft 2in (9.50m)
Armament: 8 x SS-N-12 Sandbox SSM; 2 x SA-N-3 Goblet SAM; 2 x SA-N-4 Gecko (not in *Novorossiysk*); 12 x SA-N-9 (*Novorossiysk* only); 4 x 76.2mm DP guns; 8 x 30mm Gatling CIWS; 10 x 21in (533mm) torpedo tubes; 1 x SUW-N-1 ASW RL; 2 x RBU-6000 ASW RL
Propulsion: Geared turbines, 200,000shp; 4 propellers
Performance: Speed 32 knots; range 13,500nm (25,018km) at 18 knots
Complement: 1,600 total
Air Wing: 12-13 Yakovlev Yak-38 "Forger A/B"; 14-17 Kamov Ka-25 "Hormone-A"/"Helix-A" and "Hormone-B"/"Helix-C"

Background: The primary mission of these ships is ASW, for which they can carry a maxium of 17 helicopters; but their 13 Yak-38 "Forger" strike aircraft, their other on-board weapons systems and the capabilities of other ships in their Battle Group would enable them to be used for sea denial and sea-control missions, as well. There is a long, narrow hangar and the flight-deck is angled at 4.5deg to port, but does not have a "ski-jump", as the "Forger" does not seem to use rolling take-offs.

Unlike Western carriers the Kiev class have a heavy weapons fit. For air defence there are two SA-N-3 launchers, one at either end of the superstructure and two SA-N-4 launchers. There are also two twin 76mm DP gun mounts, one on the forecastle the other at the aft end of the superstructure, as well as the usual plethora of 30mm Gatling CIWS, with eight turrets giving a good all-round protection. For ASW there is an SUW-N-1 launcher forward, two RBU-6000 ASW rocket-launchers and ten torpedo tubes.

The first two ships are essentially identical, but the third-of-class, *Novorossiysk*, has minor differences. One of the most notable differences is that she does not mount the SA-N-4 system, the space available being used for the newer SA-N-9 VLS. There are also small variations in the electronics fit and the flight-deck layout.

Kiev and *Novorossiysk* are deployed with the Northern Fleet and *Minsk* with the Pacific Fleet. In the event of hostilities during the Cold War their role would almost certainly have been to protect Soviet SSBN bastions in the Barents Sea in the West and in the Sea of Okhotsk in the East.They would also have undertaken offensive forays against NATO ASW barrier forces in such critical areas as the Greenland-Iceland-United Kingdom (GIUK) gap.

Above: The Soviet aircraft carrier *Novorossiysk* shows the different approach taken by Soviet naval designers, who have devoted the entire foredeck to a very substantial array of weapons. Also, the superstructure is covered with a wide range of antennas, with further radio antennas at various points on the deck-edge and in the bow area.

Above: *Minsk*, second ship of the Kiev class, lying peacefully at anchor with one Yak-38 Forger coming in to land and a second at the forward end of the flight-deck.

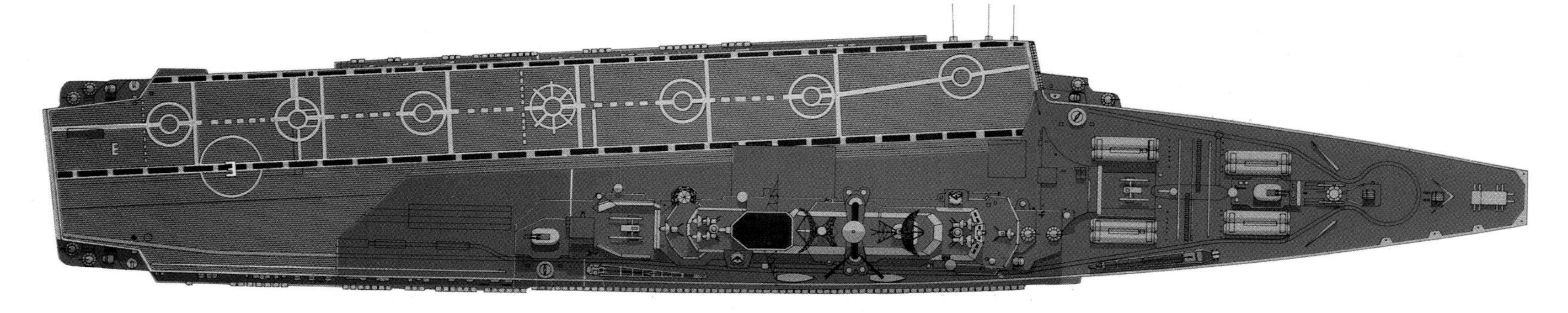

Above: This deck plan of the original *Kiev* shows the offset flight-deck, the landing-spots for the Yak-38 Forger aircraft, the lift and the large area devoted to weapons systems and superstructure.

Modified KIEV class (USSR)

Origin: USSR
Ships in Class: *Admiral Gorshkov*
Displacement: 38,000 tons (38,608 tonnes) standard; 45,000 tons (45,720 tonnes) full load
Dimensions: Length 895ft 7in (273.15m); Beam — Hull 107ft 3in (32.71m); Flight Deck 173ft 9in (53m); Draught 32ft 8in (9.96m)
Armament: 12 × SS-N-12 SSM; 24 × SA-N-9 VLS SAM; 2 × 100mm DP guns; 8 × 30mm CIWS; 2 × RBU-1200 ASW RL
Propulsion: Geared turbines, 200,000shp; 4 propellers
Performance: Speed 31.5 knots; range 13,500nm (25,018km) at 18 knots
Complement: 1,600 total
Air Wing: 13 Yakovlev Yak-38 ''Forger''; 17 Kamov Ka-27 ''Helix-A'' (ASW); 2 Ka-32 ''Helix-D'' (SAR/Utility); 3 Ka-25 ''Hormone-B'' (targetting)

Background: The long-awaited fourth ship of the Kiev class has the same hull and propulsion systems as her three predecessors. She took no less than six years to fit out following her launch, due to her many different weapons and electronic systems. The most noticeable visual difference is the fitting of two very large antenna arrays above the bridge. The *Sky Watch* radar system has four fixed planar arrays, while above that is a huge cylindrical array for the *Cake Stand* air control/TACAN system. These and other new electronics systems also appear on the later Kuznetsov class and it is now clear that *Gorshkov* was acting as a test-bed for these complex systems.

Gorshkov carries a substantial Air Wing, although it is still nowhere near as large as those on modern US Navy carriers. The strike element is provided by thirteen Yak-38 ''Forgers''; the ASW component comprises seventeen Ka-27 ''Helix-A'' helicopters. The normal complement also includes two aircraft for search-and-rescue (Ka-32 ''Helix-D'') and three for over-the-horizon weapons targetting (Ka-25 ''Hormone-B'').

Above: Comparison of the armament on the foredeck of *Gorshkov* (above) with that of *Novorssiysk* (left) clearly shows some immediate differences in terms of weapons configuration.

The weapons fit is somewhat different from the earlier members of the class. Twelve SS-N-12 *Sandbox* missile launchers are mounted, four more than in the earlier ships, but without any reloads. The long-range SA-N-3 SAM launchers have been replaced by SA-N-9 VLS silos. The two twin 76.2mm DP gun mounts on the earlier ships have been replaced by two single 100mm mounts. The SUW-N-1 ASW RL, RBU-6000 RLs and the torpedo tubes have been deleted, and ASW armament now comprises two of the new RBU-1200 ASW rocket launchers.

It would seem that there have been problems with the airflow over the flight-deck in the basic design, starting with the *Kiev*. The weapons on the foredeck obviously cause turbulence over the flight-deck, a problem which is exacerbated by the low freeboard. During her first refit *Minsk* had air-deflecting plates installed behind the after SS-N-12 launchers and a new rounded edge was fitted to the the forward end of the flight-deck. On *Gorshkov* even more care has been devoted to sorting out the obvious airflow problems. A new type of movable air deflector has been installed, while the forward edge of the flight-deck is even more rounded and the sponson for the port forward Gatling CIWS has been removed.

KITTY HAWK class (USA)

Origin: USA
Ships in Class: *Kitty Hawk* (CV-63); *Constellation* (CV-64); *America* (CV-66); *John F. Kennedy* (CV-67)
Displacement: 60,000 tons (61,061 tonnes) standard; 81,800 tons (83,109 tonnes) full load
Dimensions: Length 1,045ft 9in (318.95m); Beam — Hull 129ft 9in (39.57m); Flight Deck 252ft 0in (76.86m); Draught 37ft 4in (11.38m)
Armament: 3 x Mk 29 launchers for Sea Sparrow SAM; 3 x 20mm Mk 15 CIWS
Propulsion: Geared turbines, 280,000shp; 4 propellers
Performance: Speed 33 knots; range 4,000nm (7,413km) at 30 knots
Complement: 2,902 Ship's Company, 2,490 Air Wing
Air Wing: 20 Grumman F-14A Tomcat; 24 McDonnell-Douglas F/A-18A Hornet; 10 Grumman A-6E Intruder; 4 Grumman KA-6D Intruder; 4 Grumman EA-6B Prowler; 4 Grumman E-2C Hawkeye; 10 Lockheed S-3A Viking; 6 Sikorsky SH-3H Sea King

Background: USS *Kitty Hawk* (CV-63) and USS *Constellation* (CV-64) were ordered as improved versions of the Forrestal class incorporating some significant advances. The flight-deck area was slightly greater and the layout of the lifts was altered to improve aircraft handling, with the port-side lift moved aft so that it could still be used during landing operations. Also, the centre lift was moved forward of the island so that two lifts could be used to support the forward catapults. All lifts had an amended shape to enable larger aircraft to be carried.

There was a gap of four years between the laying down of USS *Constellation* and that of the third ship, USS *America* (CV-66). As a result, this latter carrier was able to incorporate further improvements and her dimensions are marginally different from the others in her class. These included a newer sonar system, the SQS-23, and the first integrated Combat Information Center (CIC) and airborne ASW control centre.

In 1963 it was decided to lay down a new nuclear-propelled carrier in FY64, but Congress would not agree to the cost and it was eventually agreed to build a new conventionally-powered ship to a modifed *Kitty Hawk* design. This carrier, USS *John F. Kennedy* (CV-67) has dimensions and displacement virtually identical to those of USS *America*, and she is normally grouped as a member of the Kitty Hawk

Left: USS *Kitty Hawk* operating in the Pacific Ocean, with a large part of her air wing laid out with parade-ground precision on the flight-deck. A solitary EW EA-3B Skywarrior, (forward aircraft, starboard side) dwarfs all other aircraft.

Right: USS *America* in the Indian Ocean. Conventionally-powered, she was commissioned in 1965 and is due to undergo a Service Life Extension Program (SLEP) refit from 1996 to 1999 which will enable her to remain a viable unit well into the next century.

Below: USS *America* carries: (A) 1x8 Mk 29 Sea Sparrow SAM (Mk 15 Phalanx CIWS on port side); (B) Mk 15 Phalanx CIWS; (C) 2x8 Mk 29 Sea Sparrow SAM. Electronics include: (1) SQS-23 sonar; (2) LN-66 navigation radar; (3) SPS-49A long-range radar; (4) SPS-10F surface radar; (5) URN-25 Tacan; (6) SPN-35A approach radar; (7) SPS-48C 3-D air search radar; (8) OE-83 SATCOM system; (9) Mk 91 director for Sea Sparrow.

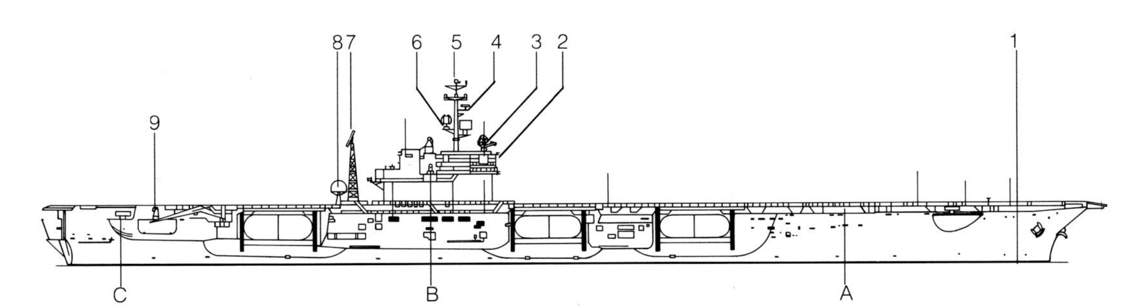

class. Visually she can be distinguished by a canted stack, intended to carry corrosive exhaust gasses clear of the flight-deck, and by the shape of the forward part of the angled deck.

USS *John F. Kennedy* and USS *America* normally serve in the Atlantic Fleet, with frequent forays into the Mediterranean Sea, and the other two in the Pacific Fleet. All four are expected to serve well into the 21st Century.

Below: This fine shot of USS *John F. Kennedy* gives an impression of the huge area of the flightdeck, which is 1,047ft (320m) in length and 252ft (77m) in width at its widest point. Note, too, the four catapults; three of which are 295ft (90m) long and the fourth 310ft (94.5m).

ADMIRAL KUZNETSOV class (USSR)

Origin: USSR
Ships in Class: *Kuznetsov; Varyag*
Displacement: 65,000 tons (66,040 tonnes) full load
Dimensions: Length 984ft 3in (301m); Beam — Flight Deck 239ft 5in (73m); Draught not known
Armament: 16 × SS-N-19 SSM; 18 × SA-N-9 SAM; ? × 30mm Gatling CIWS; 2 × RBU-12000 ASW RL
Propulsion: Steam, 200,000shp; 4 propellers
Performance: Speed 30 + knots
Complement: not known
Air Wing: Approximately 60 (see notes below) Sukhoi Su-27 "Flanker" or Mikoyan-Gurevich MiG-29 "Fulcrum"; Kamov Ka-27 "Helix-A, -B and -C"

Background: With the *Kuznetsov*, Soviet carrier design has moved to a new level, much more akin to Western design practice. She has a large, full-length flight-deck, with an angled portion offset at some 10deg to port, and a large 12deg "ski-jump". However, continuing their innovative approach to carrier practice, the Soviet designers have employed these facilities not to improve the take-off load of STOVL aircraft, but to enable CTOL aircraft to be launched without the use of a catapult.

Kuznetsov is large, with a 65,000 ton (66,040 tonne) displacement, although this is 10,000 tons (10,160 tonnes) less than the early Western estimates. According to Soviet sources, she is intended to carry an Air Wing of some 60 aircraft, which will almost certainly consist of a mixture of helicopters and navalized CTOL aircraft. A possible composition might be:

- Two squadrons, each of 10-12 Su-27 "Fencers" in the air defence role.
- Two squadrons, each of 10-12 MiG-29 "Fulcrums", in the attack role, with a secondary air defence role, if required.
- One squadron of 4-6 AEW aircraft.
- One squadron of 8-10 helicopters for SAR, communications and light attack missions.

Navalized versions of both the Su-27 and MiG-29 have already been evaluated with great success on board *Kuznetsov*, and have shown that they can operate over the "ski-jump" without any problems. A run of about 590ft (180m) is required when fully-loaded, reducing to some 330ft (100m) with the aircraft in a "clean" configuration.

Armament of the Kuznetsov class includes SS-N-19 *Shipwreck* SSMs (16 launchers), SA-N-9 vertically-launched SAMs (18 launchers) and the SA-N-11 close-in air defence system (eight launchers). No DP guns have been seen, but there are the usual 30mm Gatling CIWS mounts.

The Soviet Navy is clearly proud of this latest addition to its Fleet and has released an unprecedented amount of photographs showing the flight deck and the aircraft trials. The second ship of the class, *Varyag* will enter service in 1992.

A new carrier, *Ul'yanovsk*, is currently under construction. Of an entirely new design, she will displace 75,000 (76,200 tonnes) and will have a conventional flat flight-deck, with steam catapults rather than a "ski-jump" for take-off. She will be nuclear-powered and should enter service in about 1995. According to Soviet sources she will be "the last" carrier built for the Soviet Navy, although this seems somewhat improbable.

Above: The Soviets have always taken an independent approach to carrier design and never more so than with their latest carriers. The "ski-jump" on *Kuznetsov* is used to launch CTOL aircraft, e.g. the MiG-29 and Su-27.

MOSKVA class (USSR)

Origin: USSR
Ships in Class: *Moskva*; *Leningrad*
Displacement: 15,500 tons (15,748 tonnes) standard; 19,200 tons (19,507 tonnes) full load
Dimensions: Length 623ft 4in (190.11m); Beam — Hull 85ft 3in (26m); Flight Deck 111ft 9in (34.08m); Draught 24ft 9in (7.55m)
Armament: 2 × SA-N-3 Goblet SAM; 4 × 57mm DP guns; 1 × SUW-N-1 ASW RL; 2 × RBU-6000 ASW RL
Propulsion: Geared turbines, 100,000shp; 2 propellers
Performance: Speed 30 knots; range 14,000nm (25,945km) at 12 knots
Complement: 850 total
Air Wing: 14 Kamov Ka-27, "Hormone-A, -B, or -C"

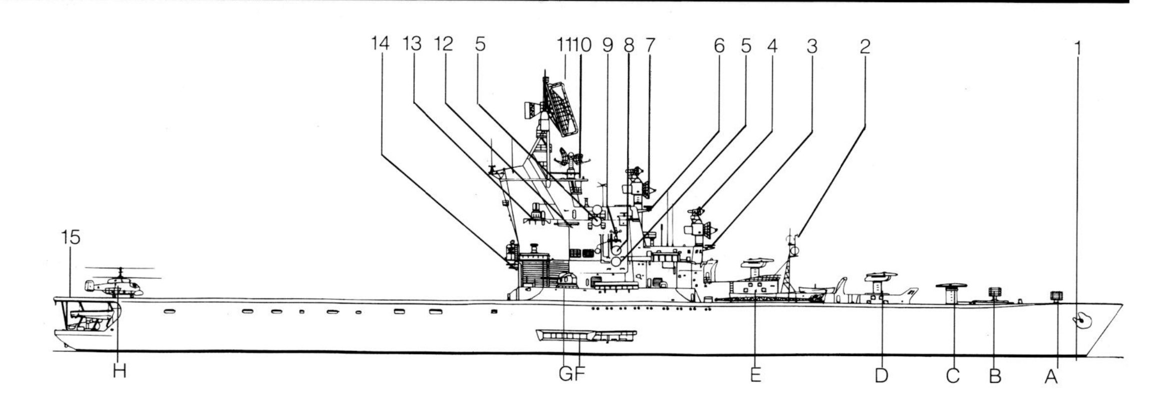

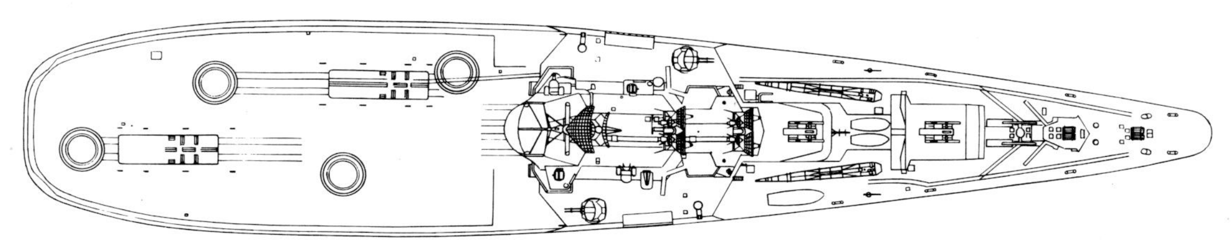

Above: Moskva class systems include: (A) RBU-6000 ASW launcher; (B) RBU-6000; (C) SUW-N-1 ASW launcher; (D) 1x2 SA-N-3 SAM; (E) 1x2 SA-N-3; (F) space for torpedoes; (G) 2x2 57mm AA gun; (H) Ka-25 Helo. Electronic systems include: (1) hull sonar; (2) DF loops; (3) Don-2 nav radar; (4) Headlight-A SAM radar; (5) Side Globe EW system; (6) Don-2; (7) Headlight-A; (8) Bell Top EW; (9) Bell Clout EW; (10) Head Net-C search radar; (11) Top Sail search radar; (12) Bell Slam EW; (13) Muff Cob fire control radar; (14) Don-2; (15) VD sonar.

Background: The ASW cruiser *Moskva* was the first Soviet warship to carry an Air Wing and set a pattern for innovative carrier design, which has been sustained to this day. The design may have been influenced by Western designs of the early-1960s, for example, France's *Jeanne d'Arc*, but the Soviet ships are much larger, operate many more aircraft and are generally more capable.

The Moskva class were designed to hunt and destroy US SSBNs operating in the eastern Mediterranean. However, they have also helped to train Soviet Navy ships' crews and aviators in the operation of large numbers of aircraft at sea. They have thus provided an essential stepping-stone to the true aircraft carriers of the Kiev and Kuznetsov classes.

The primary ASW weapon for this ship is the Kamov Ka-25 "Hormone" helicopter, of which up to 18 can be accommodated in the large hangar. This is served by two lifts, which are somewhat narrow and restrict operation to the "Hormone"; unfortunately larger helicopters such as the newer "Helix" thus cannot be handled.

Unlike most other carrier designs the *Moskvas* have a large forward superstructure, which houses a comprehensive outfit of ASW and air defence sensors and weapons.

Above: *Moskva* with Kamov Ka-25 Hormone-As spotted on the flightdeck. These ships were designed to destroy US SSBNs in the Mediterranean.

Origin: USA
Ships in Class: *Nimitz* (CVN-68); *Dwight D. Eisenhower* (CVN-69); *Carl Vinson* (CVN-70)
Displacement: 81,600 tons (82,905 tonnes) standard; 93,900 tons (95,402 tonnes) full load
Dimensions: Length 1,091ft 9in (332.98m); Beam — Hull 134ft 2in (40.92m); Flight Deck 253ft (77.16m); Draught 37ft 1in (11.31m)
Armament: 3 x Mk 29 launchers for Sea Sparrow SAM; 3 x 20mm Mk 15 CIWS (CVN-70 has 4)
Propulsion: Nuclear, 280,000shp; 4 propellers
Performance: Speed 30 + knots
Complement: 3,660 Ship's Company, 2,626 Air Wing
Air Wing: 24 Grumman F-14A Tomcat; 24 McDonnell-Douglas F/A-18A Hornet; 10 Grumman A-6E Intruder; 4 Grumman KA-6D Intruder; 4 Grumman EA-6B Prowler; 4 Grumman E-2C Hawkeye; 10 Lockheed S-3A Viking; 6 Sikorsky SH-3H Sea King

Background: When the time came to replace the Midway class carriers there was no doubt that the success of the USS *Enterprise* (CVN-65) indicated that nuclear-propulsion provided the best answer, even though the capital costs of construction were enormous. Indeed, Congress had already insisted that the USS *John F. Kennedy* (CV-67) should be powered by fuel-oil rather than nuclear reactors. However, there had been many advances since the construction of CVN-65, not least being that the eight A2W reactors used in the earlier ship could be replaced by just two A4W reactors, giving the same power. Furthermore, the uranium cores needed to be replaced only every thirteen years — much less often than on the earlier ship.

Right: USS *Nimitz* (left) and USS *Eisenhower* (right) sharing a jetty. The decks and hulls of these carriers are constructed of extra-strong, high-tensile steel and vital spaces are protected by Kevlar composite armour.

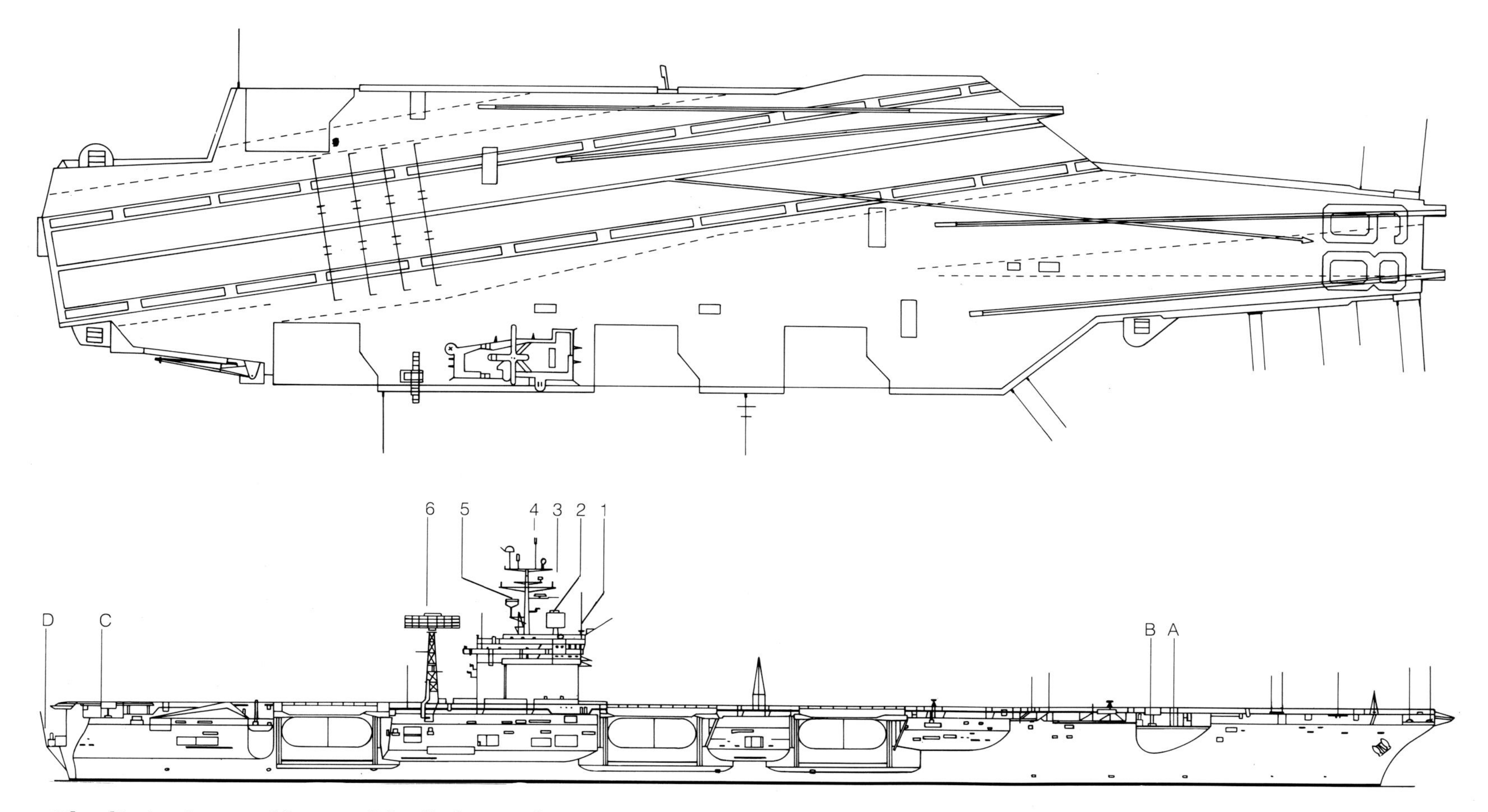

The dimensions and layout of the flight-deck on the Nimitz class are virtually identical with those on USS *John F. Kennedy*, the last of the Kitty Hawk class. However, in comparison with USS *Enterprise*, the reduction in the number of reactors permitted major improvements in the internal arrangements below hangar-deck level. The propulsion machinery is divided between two rooms, with some of the magazines in the space between them, and there is a 20 per cent increase in the volume of aviation fuel, munitions and stores that can be carried.

The combat power concentrated in these hulls is enormous, but this requires a large amount of equipment and manpower, too. There are 86 aircraft and 6,286 men — a major concentration of resources and a very attractive target in a major conflict. Also, the ships are extremely expensive: the two ships ordered in FY83 costing $6,559 million (at 1983 prices), which does not even include the cost of the Air Wing!

USS *Nimitz* is scheduled to last until at least 2020, the other two ships in this class even longer.

Above: USS *Nimitz* carries a range of short range defensive weapons including: (A) 1x8 Mk 29 Sea Sparrow SAM; (B) 2x1 Mk 15 Phalanx CIWS; (C) 2x8 Mk 29 Sea Sparrow SAM. (D) 2x1 Mk 15 Phalanx CIWS. Her sophisticated electronics suite includes: (1) LN-66 navigation radar; (2) SPS-48B long-range air surveillance radar; (3) SPS-10F surface search radar; (4) URN-20 Tacan system; (5) SPS-49 2-D air search radar; (6) SPS-43A long-range air search radar. The four deck elevators and four catapults are also visible in this view.

Above: The nuclear-powered carrier USS *Eisenhower* normally operates with the Atlantic Fleet and frequently undertakes Mediterranean deployments. Her nuclear core gives a cruising range of some 1,000,000nm.

PRINCIPE DE ASTURIAS class (Spain)

Origin: Spain
Ships in Class: *Principe de Asturias* (R-11)
Displacement: 16,200 tons (16,459 tonnes)
Dimensions: Length 640ft 1in (195.22m); Beam — Hull 80ft 1in (24.42m); Flight Deck 98ft 4in (30m); Draught 22ft (6.71m)
Armament: 4 x Meroka 20mm gun systems
Propulsion: Gas turbines, 46,400shp; 1 propeller
Performance: Speed 26-27 knots; range 6,500nm (12,046km) at 20 knots
Complement: 744 total
Air Wing: 6-8 McDonnell Douglas EAV-8B Harrier II; 12-14 Sikorsky SH-60B Seahawk; Sikorsky SH-3D/G Sea King and Agusta-Bell AB.212

Background: From 1967 onwards the Spanish Navy operated a single aircraft carrier, the *Dedalo,* a converted former US Navy Cleveland-class cruiser. She carried an Air Wing of five AV-8S Harriers (designated *Matador* in Spanish service), eight SH-3D Sea Kings and four AB-212s. However, this old ship was only intended to fill the gap while a more modern design was selected and built.

In the late-1960s the US Navy produced a concept for a "sea-control ship" (SCS), which was intended to fulfil ASW and air superiority missions in low-threat areas. Of relatively small size and without the highly-sophisticated electronics found on the larger US carriers, the SCS was supposed to be cheap to build and maintain, and easy to operate. The US project came to naught, but the Spanish Navy considered that the design met their needs and in 1977 a contract was placed with the main Spanish shipyard, Bazan, at El Ferrol.

The ship is built around her aviation facilities, which include a full-width hangar occupying the aft two-thirds of the ship. A major feature not in the original SCS design is a full-width 12deg "ski-jump", which enables the AV-8B and EAV-8B aircraft to carry out rolling take-offs at full load. To maintain the policy of simplicity, only a single shaft is fitted and the electronic fit is austere by modern standards. Fixed armament in this class comprises four Spanish-designed Meroka 20mm CIWS.

The Air Wing comprises some 20 aircraft. The strike element is produced by 6-8 EAV-8B Harrier IIs, although AV-8E Matadors will doubtless also be used helicopter component of up to 14 aircraft, the majority being SH-60B Sea Hawk helicopters, together with SH-3Ds, some of which will be configured for AEW operations.

The Spanish Navy seems to have invested well, having obtained a very capable carrier at a reasonable price. *Principe de Asturias* will be the flagship of the Spanish "Battle Group *Alfa*", which is committed to NATO operations in the North Atlantic. The only weakness in the Spanish plan is that with only one carrier there will be no cover when the ship goes in for long refits. All the logic, therefore, points to a second carrier, although whether this can be afforded is another matter.

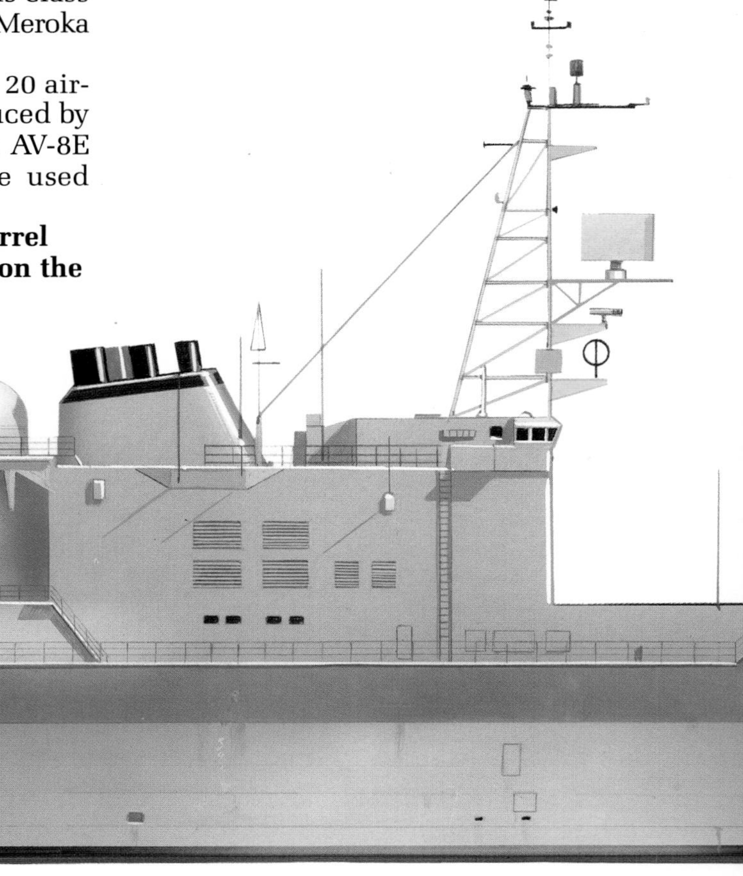

Right: Unlike the carriers in other small navies, the Spanish *Principe de Asturias* is thoroughly modern and custom-built for her mission. The design was based upon that of the US Navy's proposed Sea Control Ship, but updated and adapted to Spanish requirements. She is powered by General Electric gas-turbines and her armament consists of four 12-barrel Meroka CIWS, with two turrets on the quarterdeck and two forward.

THEODORE ROOSEVELT class (USA)

Origin: USA
Ships in Class: *Theodore Roosevelt* (CVN-71; *Abraham Lincoln* (CVN-72); *George Washington* (CVN-73); *John C Stennis* (CVN-74); *United States* (CVN-75)
Displacement: 73,973 tons (75,156 tonnes) standard; 96,836 tons (98,385 tonnes) full load
Dimensions: Length 1,092ft 2in (330.11m); Beam — Hull 134ft 2in (40.92m); Flight Deck 256ft 9in (78.31m); Draught 38ft 4in (11.69m)
Armament: 3 x Mk 29 launchers for Sea Sparrow SAM; 4 x 20mm Mk 15 CIWS
Propulsion: Nuclear, 280,000shp; 4 propellers
Performance: Speed 30 + knots
Complement: 3,508 Ship's Company, 2,512 Air Wing
Air Wing: 24 (CVN-71 = 20) Grumman F-14A Tomcat; 24 (CVN = 20) McDonnell-Douglas F/A-18A Hornet; 10 (CVN-71 = 20) Grumman A-6E Intruder; 4 (CVN-71 = 5) Grumman KA-6D Intruder; 4 (CVN-71 = 5) Grumman EA-6B Prowler; 4 (CVN-71 = 5) Grumman E-2C Hawkeye; 10 Lockheed S-3A Viking; 6 Sikorsky SH-3H Sea King

Background: These are the mightiest and most powerful warships ever built. The first-of-class, USS *Theodore Roosevelt* (CVN-71), was originally intended to be the fourth member of the Nimitz class, but because the subject of considerable political wrangling during the Carter Administration. Shipyard problems had led to escalating costs and an attempt was made to stop construction of the fourth unit in favour of either a smaller, conventionally-powered design (designated CVV), or a repeat of the conventionally-powered USS *John F. Kennedy* (CV-67). However, the CVV design was never popular with the US Navy and they managed to resist the pressures until President Reagan replaced Carter. The fourth unit was then laid down.

The design is an improved version of the Nimitz class, with new, low-pressure catapults and better self-protection, including Kevlar armour over vital spaces. The total aviation payload carried is over 14,909 tons (15,148 tonnes).

The Air Wing consists of 86 aircraft, varying in role from strike, interceptor/fighter and attack to EW, ASW and in-flight refuelling. This amounts to a balanced tactical air force, which is stronger and more effective than most *national* air forces in their entirety. But this must be seen in the context of US naval aviation as a whole, which in FY91 had a total strength of 5,036 aircraft, of which 3,659 were operated by the Navy and 1,377 by the Marine Corps.

Two more ships of the Theodore Roosevelt class are planned for delivery in 2000 and 2003.

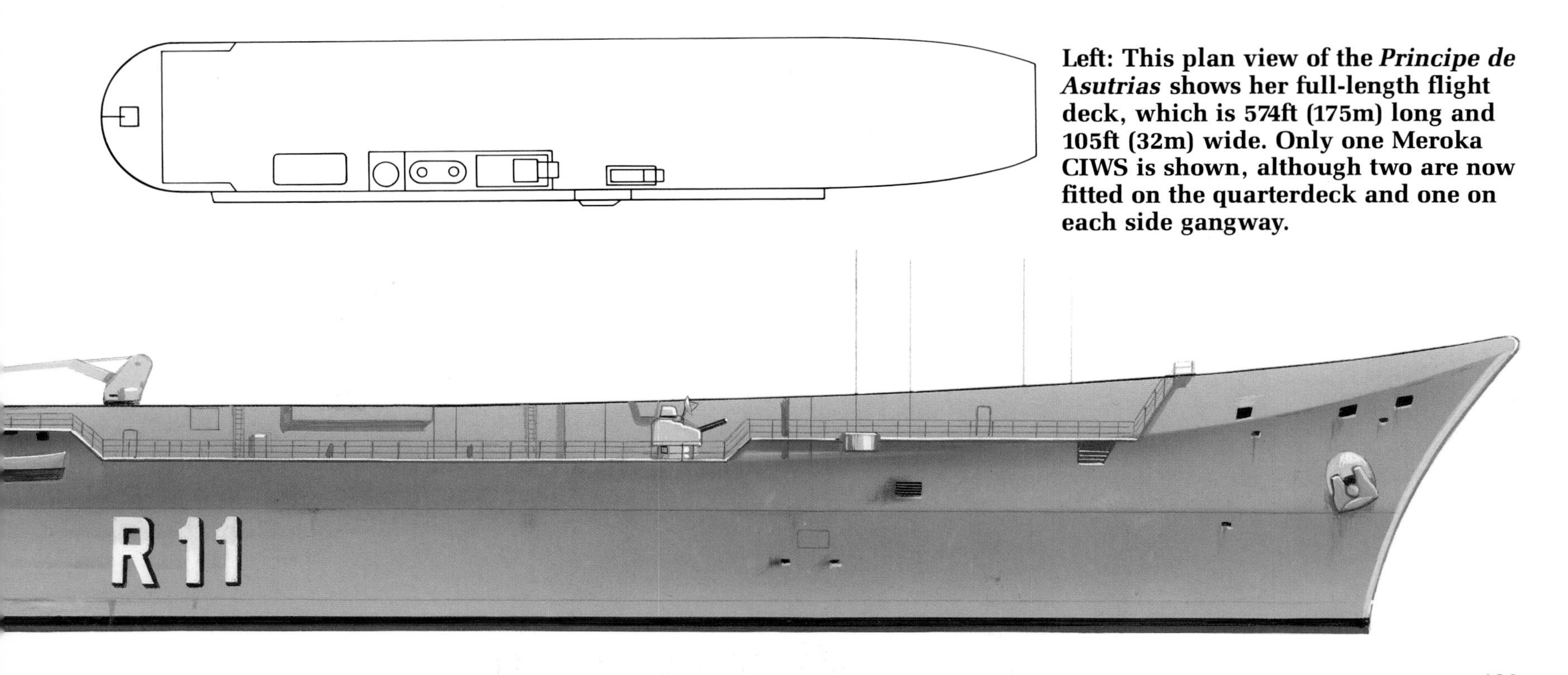

Left: This plan view of the *Principe de Asutrias* shows her full-length flight deck, which is 574ft (175m) long and 105ft (32m) wide. Only one Meroka CIWS is shown, although two are now fitted on the quarterdeck and one on each side gangway.

SAN GIORGIO class (Italy)

Origin: Italy
Ships in Class: *San Giorgio* (L-9892); *San Marco* (L-9893)
Displacement: 5,000 tons (5,080 tonnes) standard; 7,665 tons (7,787 tonnes) full load
Dimensions: Length 437ft 3in (133.36m); Beam 67ft 3in (20.51m); Draught 17ft 2in (5.23m)
Armament: 1 x Oto Melara 76mm DP; 2 x 20mm AA; 2 x 12.7mm MG
Propulsion: Diesel, 16,800bhp; 2 propellers
Performance: Speed 21 knots (sustained); range 4,500nm (8,339km) at 20 knots
Complement: 160 Ship's Company (plus 400 troops)
Air Wing: 5 CH-47 or Agusta/Sikorsky SH-3D Sea King

Background: The Italian Navy operated two elderly ex-US Navy landing-ships for many years; but their age, coupled with an increasing commitment to rapid deployment of the *San Marco* marine unit and to disaster relief, led to a requirement for newer and more capable amphibious warfare ships. This has resulted in a most interesting design of roll-on/roll-off ship, with a full-length flight-deck.

These 7,665 ton (7,787 tonne) ships are primarily intended for amphibious warfare operations, for which they can carry 400 troops, with their vehicles being accommodated in a large hangar below the flight-deck. There is a docking well with a stern ramp and the ships can also beach and land troops and vehicles over a bow ramp. Three large LCMs are accommodated in the docking well and three slightly smaller LCVPs are carried on davits on the upper deck. There is also extensive stowage for refrigerated stores, dry stores and aviation fuel.

The aircraft are stowed on the flight deck. The normal complement would be five helicopters, either Boeing CH-47 Chinooks, SH-3Ds, or, in the future, EH-101s.

The second ship, *San Marco*, was partially funded by the Ministry of Civil Protection; consequently her disaster relief facilities are even more extensive than those on *San Giorgio*.

Below: *San Giorgio*. Her sister-ship *San Marco*, was sent to the Gulf to provide hospital and evacuation facilities. The design is a success and a third ship has been ordered.

TARAWA class (USA)

Origin: USA
Ships in Class: *Tarawa* (LHA-1); *Saipan* (LHA-2); *Belleau Wood* (LHA-3); *Nassau* (LHA-4); *Peleliu* (LHA-5)
Displacement: 25,120 tons (25,522 tonnes) standard; 39,300 tons (39,929 tonnes) full load
Dimensions: Length 834ft (254.37m); Beam — Hull 106ft (32.33m); Flight Deck 131ft 9in (40.18m); Draught 25ft 9in (7.85m)
Armament: 2 × 127mm Mk 45 DP; 2 × 20mm Mk 15 CIWS; 6 × 20mm Mk 67 AA
Propulsion: Geared turbines, 77,000shp; 2 propellers
Performance: Speed 24 knots; range 10,000nm (18,532km) at 20 knots
Complement: 940 Ship's Company and Air Wing, 1,924 Troops
Air Wing: 16 Boeing-Vertol CH-46 Sea Knight; 6 Sikorsky CH-53 Sea Stallion; 4 Bell UH-1 Iroquois/AH-1 Sea Cobra

Above: The Tarawa class amphibious assault ships combine in one hull the tasks previously performed by helicopter landing ships (LPH) and dock landing ships (LPD). They carry up to 38 helicopters and four LCUs.

Background: By the 1960s the US Navy and Marine Corps found themselves with two types of amphibious warfare ship. One was the specialized helicopter assault ship (LHA) of the Iwo Jima class, the other the dock-type ship (LPD) of the Austin and Raleigh classes. It was therefore decided to combine these two into one type of amphibious assault ship, the Tarawa class, which was much larger, with a displacement of 39,300 tons (39,929 tonnes).

These highly capable ships incorporate both a hangar and a docking-well, and there are nine landing spots for the helicopters on the flight-deck. AV-8A/B Harriers are also regularly embarked. The docking-well accommodates four LCUs and four more smaller landing-craft are carried on the flight-deck.

Tarawa, Belleau Wood and *Pelelieu* normally operate with the Pacific Fleet, while *Saipan* and *Nassau* operate with the Atlantic Fleet. They are almost invariably roled as flagships and because of this role there are extensive facilities for both the Commander Amphibious Task Group (CATG) and the Landing Force Commander (LFC) and their respective staffs.

UL'YANOVSK class (USSR)

Origin: USSR
Ships in Class: *Ul'yanovssk*
Displacement: c.75,120 tons (76,200 tonnes)
Dimensions: Length 1050ft (320m); Beam and Draught not known
Armament: not known
Propulsion: PWR nuclear reactors
Performance: not known
Complement: not known
Air Wing: Probably around 65-70 aircraft, including Su-27 Flanker, MiG-29 Fulcrum, Su-25 Frogfoot and Ka-27 and Ka-32 Helix

Background: Currently under construction and expected to launch in 1991, *Ul'yanovsk* further demonstrates Soviet determination to develop a powerful naval aviation capability. Larger than the Kuznetsov class, the Ul'yanovsk class will be nuclear powered and equipped with conventional steam catapults rather than a ski-jump.

The mix of aircraft is yet to be revealed, although navalised versions of the Su-27 Flanker and MiG-29 Fulcrum will probably form the core of the air group. It remains to be seen whether aircraft dedicated to the strike, EW, reconnaissance, AEW and fixed-wing ASW missions will be developed.

With the current downturn in Soviet defence spending it seems unlikely that the planned class of four will be built. Some Soviet sources have indicated that *Ul'yanovsk* is the "last aircraft carrier to be built for the Soviet Navy". Just how accurate such a statement proves to be will depend to a very large extent on the progress achieved by the USSR and the USA in the delicate and contentious area of conventional arms reductions.

VIKRANT (British Majestic) class (India)

Origin: UK
Ships in Class: *Vikrant* (R-11)
Displacement: 15,700 tons (15,951 tonnes) standard; 19,500 tons (19,812 tonnes) full load
Dimensions: Length 693ft 1in (211.39m); Beam — Hull 79ft 7in (24.27m); Flight Deck 128ft 0in (39.04m); Draught 23ft 5in (7.14m)
Armament: 8 × 40mm AA
Propulsion: Geared turbines, 40,000shp; 2 propellers
Performance: Speed 24 knots; range 6,200nm (11,490km) at 23 knots, 12,000nm (22,238km) at 14 knots
Complement: 1,075 total (peace); 1,340 total (war)
Air Wing: 6 BAe Sea Harrier FRS.51; 6 Westland Sea King Mk42B; 3 Westland Sea King Mk 42C

Below: Yet another of the former British 'light fleet carriers,' INS *Vikrant* is now somewhat elderly, but is still performing a valuable role as an ASW carrier, in support of India's aim of becoming the predominant naval power in the Indian Ocean.

VIRAAT (British Hermes) class (India)

Origin: UK
Ships in Class: *Viraat* (R-22)
Displacement: 23,900 tons (24,282 tonnes) standard; 28,706 tons (29,165 tonnes) full load
Dimensions: Length 744ft 4in (227.02m); Beam — Hull 89ft 9in (27.37m); Flight Deck 160ft 1in (48.82m); Draught 28ft 9in (8.77m)
Armament: 2 × SeaCat SAM
Propulsion: Geared turbines, 76,000shp; 2 propellers
Performance: Speed 28 knots; range 6,500nm (12,046km) at 14 knots
Complement: 1,170 total
Air Wing: 6 BAe Sea Harrier FRS.51; 6 Westland Sea King Mk 42B; 3 Westland Sea King Mk 42C

Background: The former British carrier HMS *Hermes* has had a very eventful career in her time. She was laid down in 1944, but was not launched until 1953 and then spent another six years being fitted out, finally joining the Royal Navy in 1959.

At that time she was thoroughly up-to-date with steam catapults, 3-D radar, mirror landing aids and side lifts, although her 6.5deg-angled deck was somewhat less than the optimum (10-12deg), but was the best that could be achieved in a hull of her size.

In the early-1970s HMS *Hermes* was converted into a commando carrier, able to operate large numbers of helicopters and to accommodate troops. Three years later she was converted again, this time into an ASW helicopter carrier. Then, after just another three years, she was fitted with a 12deg "ski-jump", rejoining the Royal Navy in May 1981.

HMS *Hermes* was thus fully worked-up just in time for the Falklands War, where she was one of two British aircraft carriers sent South with the Task Force to recapture the Falkland Islands, while there she operated some 12 Sea Harriers and numerous helicopters.

She was paid-off in 1984 and purchased by the Indian Navy, who commissioned her on 12 May 1987 as the INS *Viraat* (Mighty). At the moment she is being operated with a similar Air Wing to that carried aboard the INS *Vikrant*; ie, six Sea Harriers, six Sea King Mk 42B ASW helicopters and three Sea King Mk 42C transports.

However, plans are now being considered to operate *Vikrant* as a helicopter carrier, thus giving *Viraat* the capacity to operate only Sea Harriers, with up to thirty being carried — a formidable fighting capability.

Viraat is now an old ship. Her hull was completed in 1945 and she has been in active service and virtually continuous operation since 1959. She uses old-fashioned black oil fuel and has a limited steaming range. Nevertheless, she remains a powerful combat ship, especially in the Indian Ocean area, and is likely to remain in service with the Indian Navy for at least another ten years, and perhaps for longer. Her eventual retirement from service will form part of the Indian Navy's ambitious modernisation plan for the 1990s. One part of this plan will include the acquisition of at least two new-build carriers.

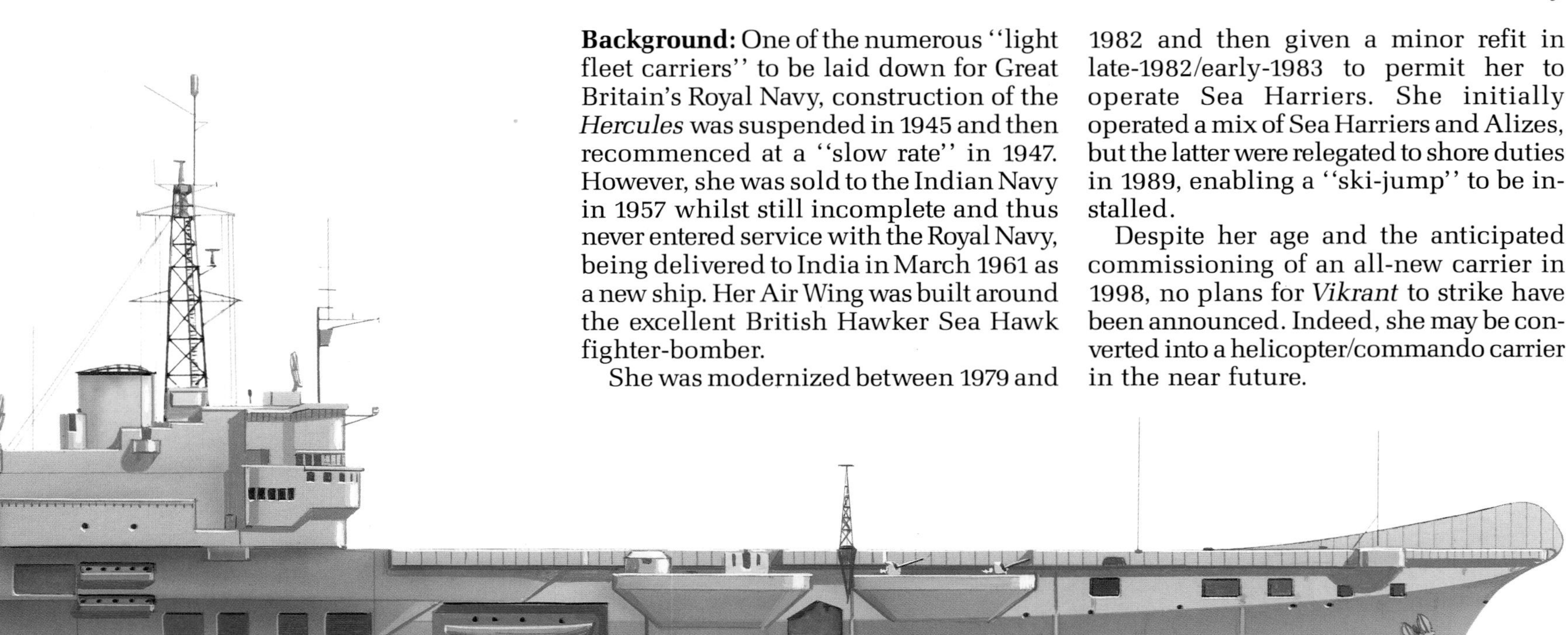

Background: One of the numerous "light fleet carriers" to be laid down for Great Britain's Royal Navy, construction of the *Hercules* was suspended in 1945 and then recommenced at a "slow rate" in 1947. However, she was sold to the Indian Navy in 1957 whilst still incomplete and thus never entered service with the Royal Navy, being delivered to India in March 1961 as a new ship. Her Air Wing was built around the excellent British Hawker Sea Hawk fighter-bomber.

She was modernized between 1979 and 1982 and then given a minor refit in late-1982/early-1983 to permit her to operate Sea Harriers. She initially operated a mix of Sea Harriers and Alizes, but the latter were relegated to shore duties in 1989, enabling a "ski-jump" to be installed.

Despite her age and the anticipated commissioning of an all-new carrier in 1998, no plans for *Vikrant* to strike have been announced. Indeed, she may be converted into a helicopter/commando carrier in the near future.

WASP class (USA)

Origin: USA
Ships in Class: *Wasp* (LHD-1); *Essex* (LHD-2); *Kearsarge* (LHD-3); *Boxer* (LHD-4)
Displacement: 28,233 tons (28,674 tonnes) standard; 40,532 tons (41,180 tonnes) full load
Dimensions: Length 844ft 2in (257.49m); Beam — Hull 106ft (32.33m); Flight Deck 140ft 1in (42.72m); Draught 26ft 6in (8.08m)
Armament: 2 × Mk 29 launchers for Sea Sparrow and RAM; 3 × 20mm Mk 15 CIWS; 8 × 12.7mm MG
Propulsion: Geared turbines, 77,000shp; 2 propellers
Performance: Speed 24 knots; range 9,500nm (17,605km) at 20 knots
Complement: 1,080 Ship's Company and Air Wing, plus 1,873 Troops
Air Wing: Assault mode — 30-32 Boeing-Vertol CH-46 Sea Knight; 6 McDonnell-Douglas AV-8B Harrier II. Carrier mode — 20 McDonnell-Douglas AV-8B Harrier II; 4-6 Sikorsky SH-60B Sea Hawk

Background: The Wasp class is an improved and even more versatile version of the Tarawa class, and can serve as either an amphibious warfare ship, or as an ASW carrier, with a combat load of 20 AV-8Bs and six SH-60Bs. The latter configuration looks suspiciously like the Sea Control Ship (SCS) concept of the 1970s, which proved so unpopular with the US Navy at that time!

One of the design criteria was maximum deck-space, which led to the decision not to install a "ski-jump" and the deletion of the two 127mm DP guns, which results in a much wider and squarer bow than in the Tarawas.

The stern gate in the Tarawa class lifts to open, but in the Wasp class it lowers as in earlier LPDs and LSDs. The flight-deck has been strengthened, using HY100 steel, and Kevlar protects vital spaces.

These are exceptionally capable ships, with an unprecedented mission flexibility. However, they are also very expensive. The original plan was to build seven to replace the Iwo-Jima class, but this was altered in the mid-1980s to a target of eleven. Of these, the first six were intended as straight additions to the overall capability of the fleet, following which the last five would replace the Iwo Jimas. However, firm plans do not extend beyond the six currently on order, although the Gulf War and its aftermath may lead to a restoration of the plans for a full eleven.

Above: USS *Wasp* can operate either in the amphibious warfare role or as an ASW/escort carrier. A 'ski-jump' was omitted to maximise deck-space.

INDEX

Note: Page numbers in **bold** or *italic* type refer to subjects in captions and illustrations. In addition, a **bold** type entry indicates the main reference to a specific ship (in chapter 7) or named aircraft (in chapter 5).

Photo Credits
Jacket (front) US DoD, (back, all four) US DoD, **Endpapers:** US DoD, **Page 1:** US DoD, **2/3:** Chris Bennett/Right Stuff Productions, **4/5:** US DoD, **6/7:** US DoD, **8:** National Archives, **9:** (both) National Archives, **10:** Fleet Air Arm Museum, **11:** (bottom left), Spanish Navy, (bottom right), Imperial War Museum, **12:** National Archives, **13:** (top) Fleet Air Arm Museum, (middle) US DoD, **14:** Fleet Air Arm Museum, **15:** US DoD, **16:** US DoD, **17:** (top) National Archives, (bottom) US DoD, **18:** (top) US DoD, (middle) National Archives, (bottom) Fleet Air Arm Museum, **19:** US DoD, **20:** National Archives, **20/21:** US DoD, **22:** (top left) US DoD, (bottom left) US DoD, **22/23:** US DoD, **24:** (top) Grumman Corporation, (bottom) Brazilian Navy, **25:** US DoD, **26/27:** Brian M. Service, **28:** (top right) Indian Navy, (bottom left) Royal Navy, **29:** Chris Bennett/Right Stuff Productions, **30:** Imperial War Museum, **31:** (top left) Imperial War Museum, (top right) US DoD, (bottom right) US DoD, **32:** (both) US DoD, **34:** US DoD, **35:** US DoD, **36:** (top left) Imperial War Museum, (top right) ECPA, (bottom right) US DoD, **37:** (both) US DoD, **38:** Imperial War Museum, **39:** Imperial War Museum, **40:** Fleet Air Arm Museum, **41:** US DoD, **42:** (both) US DoD, **43:** (both) US DoD, **44:** (all) US DoD, **46:** Rolls-Royce plc (Peter Holman), **47:** Chris Bennett/Right Stuff Productions, **48:** US DoD, **48/49:** US DoD, **50:** Royal Navy, **50/51:** Royal Navy, **51:** Chris Bennett/Right Stuff Productions, **52:** (top left) SIRPA/MER, (bottom) Brian M. Service, **53:** (top) ECPA (bottom) Indian Navy, **54/55:** US DoD, **55:** US DoD, **56:** (top left) US DoD, (bottom) Robbie Shaw, **57:** US DoD, **58:** (top left) US DoD, (middle left) US DoD, (bottom left) Robbie Shaw, **58/59:** Robbie Shaw, **60:** US DoD, **61:** (top) McDonnell Douglas, (middle) US DoD, (bottom) US DoD, **62:** (both) US DoD, **63:** (top) McDonnell Douglas, (bottom) Grumman Corporation, **64:** (both) US DoD, **65:** VA-46/US Navy, **66:** US DoD, (bottom) Grumman Corporation, **67:** US DoD, **68:** US DoD, **68/69:** US DoD, **70:** (all) US DoD, **71:** Rolls-Royce plc (Peter Holman), **72:** (top right) Katz Photos, (bottom left) US DoD, **73:** (both) US DoD, **74:** (top) Robbie Shaw, (bottom) US DoD, **75:** (both) US DoD, **76/77:** US DoD, **77:** (both) US DoD, **78:** US DoD, **78/79:** US DoD, **79:** (both) US DoD, **80:** (both) US DoD, **81:** (both) US DoD, **82:** US DoD, **83:** (both) US DoD, **84:** US DoD, **85:** (all) US DoD, **86:** US DoD, **86/87:** US DoD, **87:** (top right) Robbie Shaw, (bottom) US DoD, **88:** (both) US DoD, **89:** US DoD, **90/91:** Grumman Corporation, **92:** (both) US DoD, **93:** US DoD, **94:** (both) US DoD, **95:** (both) US DoD, **96/97:** Brian M. Service, **98:** US DoD, **99:** US DoD, **100:** (top) Robbie Shaw, (bottom) US DoD, **101:** (both) US DoD, **102/103:** US DoD, **104:** US DoD, **105:** (both) US DoD, **106:** (both) US DoD, **107:** (top left) Grumman Corporation, (bottom) Bob Munro, **108:** (both) US DoD, **109:** US DoD, **110:** (top left) ECPA, (top right) Rolls-Royce plc (Peter Holman), **111:** Rolls-Royce plc (Peter Holman), **112:** (top left) Chris Bennett/Right Stuff Productions, (bottom) US DoD, **113:** Rolls-Royce plc (Peter Holman), **114:** (top left) US DoD, (bottom) McDonnell Douglas, **115:** Brian M. Service, **116:** (both) US DoD, **116/117:** McDonnell Douglas, **118:** US DoD, **119:** US DoD, **120:** (both) US DoD, **121:** US DoD, **122/123:** Argentine Navy, **124:** US DoD, **124/125:** US DoD, **125:** AMD BA, **126:** (top right) Bob Munro, (bottom) Robbie Shaw, **127:** (all) Indian Navy, **128:** (top) ECPA, (middle) Chris Bennett/Right Stuff Productions, (bottom) US DoD, **129:** Rolls-Royce plc (Peter Holman), **130:** US DoD, **131:** (top) US DoD, (bottom) Grumman Corporation, **132:** (both) TASS, **133:** TASS, **134/135:** US DoD, **136:** (both) US DoD, **137:** (top right) US DoD, (bottom left) Katz Pictures, **138:** (top) Chris Bennett/Right Stuff Productions, (bottom three) US DoD, **139:** (top) GEC Marconi, (bottom) Rolls-Royce plc (Peter Holman), **140:** (both) US DoD, **141:** (both) US DoD, **142:** US DoD, **143:** (top) Grumman Corporation, (bottom right) Royal Navy, **144:** (both) US DoD, **145:** Katz Pictures, **147:** Royal Navy, **149:** US DoD, **150:** ECPA, **151:** EEP, **152:** US DoD, **153:** (both) US DoD, **155:** (both) Italian Navy, **156:** Royal Navy, **157:** Royal Navy, **158:** US DoD, **159:** (top) US DoD, (bottom) British Aerospace, **160:** (both) US DoD, **162:** (both) US DoD, **163:** US DoD, **164:** Novosti Press Agency (APN), **165:** US DoD, **166:** US DoD, **167:** US DoD, **170:** Italian Navy, **171:** US DoD, **173:** US DoD, **Endpapers:** US DoD